PAUL CHAUCHARD

Translated by David Noakes

THE BRAIN

PROFILE BOOKS

VISTA BOOKS · LONDON

FIRST PUBLISHED IN THIS EDITION 1962.

Library of Congress Catalog Card Number: 61-6601

Profile Books are published
in the United States by Grove Press, Inc.
64 University Place, New York 3, N.Y.

in Great Britain by Evergreen Books Ltd., London

First Published in France by Editions du Seuil, Paris, as
Le Cerveau et la Conscience

MANUFACTURED BY N.V. GRAFISCHE INDUSTRIE HAARLEM
IN THE NETHERLANDS

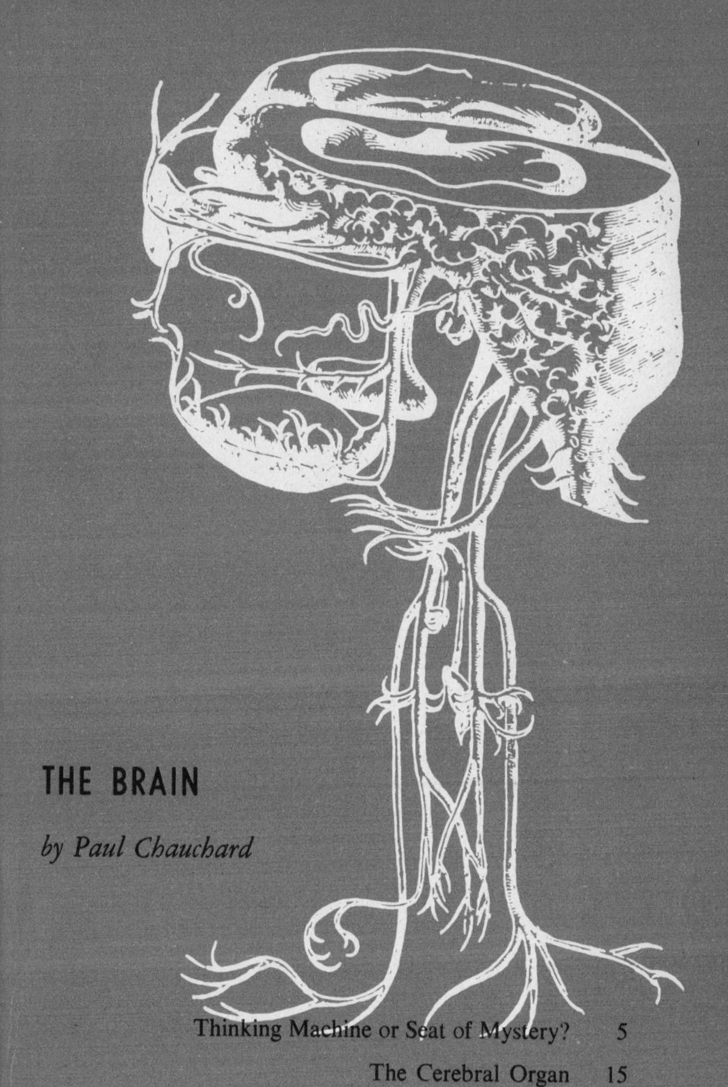

THE BRAIN

by Paul Chauchard

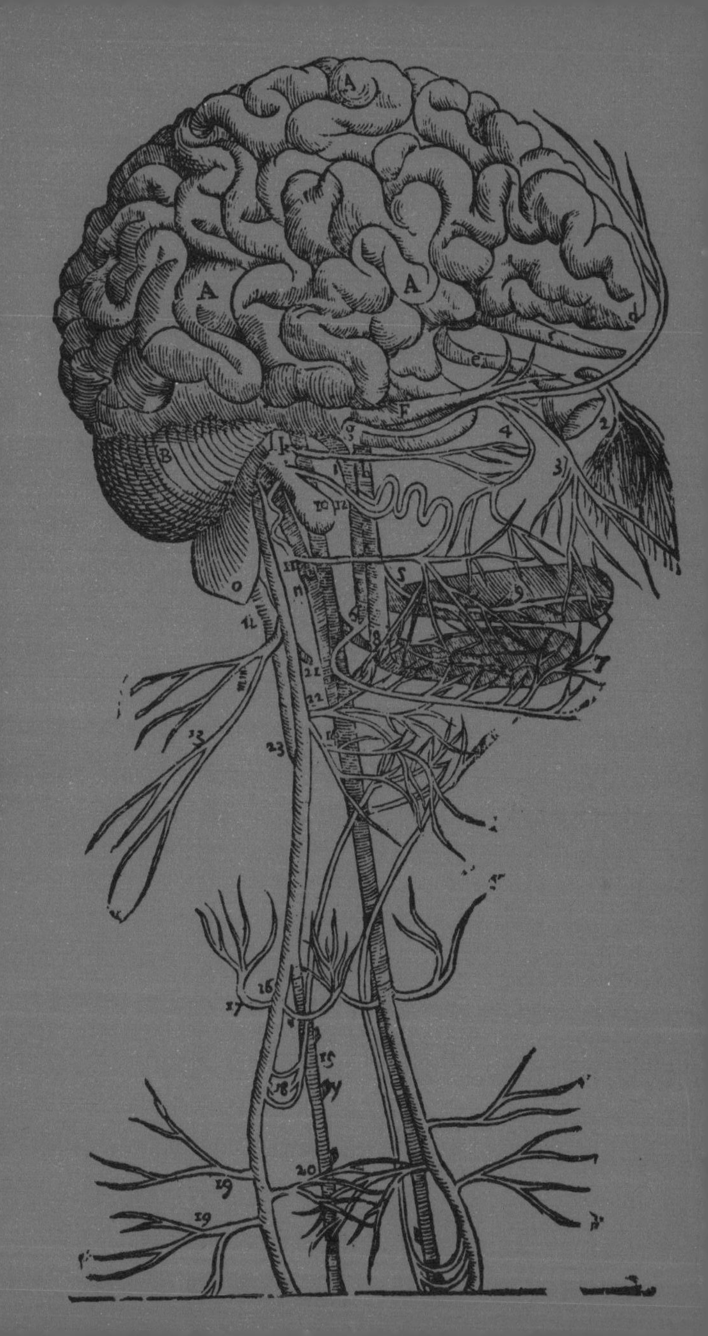
A
A
A
A
d
e
F
B
4
2
3
9
7
16
17
18
19
19
20
21
22
23

Thinking Machine or Seat Mystery?

It is hard for man to accept the idea that his brain * is just one organ among many others. True, it would seem to be of the same class as the ordinary internal parts of the body. The human brain scarcely differs from the animal brains we can inspect in the butcher's showcase. But how can we fail to look upon it as our essential organ? How can we avoid seeing it in an aura of sacred mystery connected with the origin of our species and the uniqueness of man's nature?

Nonetheless, the brain is not indispensable to life,* in the same way as, for example, an organ such as the heart. But if the brain is missing, or does not function, human life has lost that which gives it its superiority: consciousness,* will * or volition, thought. * That is where the mystery comes in: how can such an ordinary-looking organ be respensible for our psychism *?

When a stomach contracts or secretes digestive juices, when a liver produces bile, or when a kidney filters blood and excretes urine, these biological mechanisms, however marvelous they may be, seem to us to be a normal consequence of the activity of living cells. But what connection can there be between the mind and the material activity of

* The glossary, p. 171, gives the definition of all the words followed by an asterisk.

broise Paré's conception of the brain (sixteenth century).

a nerve cell? Why doesn't an animal's brain also possess that characteristic of the human brain which makes possible truly intelligent thought?

Faced with these problems posed by our brain, we are tempted to let the position we take be ruled by our philosophic and religious choices. Do we have a soul * and what is its relation to our body *? If we are unbelievers, we may tend to regard mind as a material cerebral product, a kind of secretion. If we are believers, we will see in the human brain a mechanism at the service of a spiritual soul: man differs from other animals because of his soul, not because of his brain.

The relationship between the brain and the mind or spirit cannot be understood scientifically in such a way. Though it may be legitimate at the end of this book to touch upon the philosophic problem, the important thing for the moment is to leave the realm of hypotheses, to forget about materialism * and idealism,* to stop wondering whether we have a soul, and to concern ourselves exclusively with the way in which our brain performs the psychological functions we as men possess.

To what extent is intelligence * related to the totality of the nervous system? To exactly what extent can we grasp the material processes employed by the mind in its thousand operations? To what secret equilibrium do we owe the delicate harmony of our psychological faculties? These are problems, as Lhermitte says, that disturb every man, whether in the full light of his consciousness or in the obscurity that lies behind the subconscious * threshold. What we will examine are the answers that the man of today can give to these problems.

The connection between the brain and the mind or spirit is obvious. We observe daily that anything which disturbs cerebral functioning modifies the psychism. Not only violent blows on the head and cerebral lesions but also sleep * (temporary suspension of the brain's conscious activity) cause consciousness and volition to disappear. From time immemorial, moreover, primitive man, whether prehistoric or contemporary, has testified to the importance he instinctively attributes to the brain by his worship of skulls, his cannibalistic consumption of brains, or his practice of trepanation. Man did not always connect it with the spirit, admittedly, since it was the idea of breath that the ancients associated with the idea of spirit. The Greeks attributed an important psychological role to the diaphragm (*phrén, phrenós*), lungs, and heart. Although this mistake was still made by the great philosopher Aristotle, it had been fought five hundred years before Christ by Greek naturalistic doctors – Alcmeon of Crotona, among others – whose dissections and elementary experiments made them the real founders of neurology. Even though they were unable to see how the brain made consciousness, thought, and volition possible, they nonetheless had understood that it was the organ of these functions. Between the second century A.D, when our anatomical knowledge was considerably furthered by Galen's dissections (particularly of monkey brains, which he identified too closely with men's), and the Renaissance, when Vesalius resumed research, the Scholastic refusal to observe and experiment permitted no progress.

In the seventeenth century, the philosopher Descartes had a good understanding of the nervous mechanism, considering what was known at the time. He showed it to be *reflex* *: the activation of nerve centers by messages from the senses *(sensorial message *)* resulting in the issuance of action orders. But, confusing the philosophic and the scientific points of view, he constructed a strict dichotomy between the animal seen as a machine, whose psychism could be reduced to a nervous mechanism, and man seen as mind, for whom this mechanism is at the command of the mind which sets it into action.

For many eighteenth-century philosophers, such a distinction was inadmissible. Wasn't man also a machine whose psychism should be associated with the reflex functioning of his brain? By improperly identifying the scientific problem of the cerebral conditions of human thought with the metaphysical problem of the nature of that thought, they oriented the new psychophysiology toward philosophic materialism.

In spite of a few attempts such as those of Pourfour du Petit, however, experimental neurophysiology had not yet come into being. When, at the beginning of the nineteenth century, the relationship between the physical and the moral sides of the question was dealt with for the first time objectively by Cabanis, a doctor, who refused to make the false Cartesian distinction between soul and body, this founder of modern psychophysiology had to admit our ignorance of the brain's functioning. The experimental efforts of the nineteenth century, the century of Claude Bernard, subsequently proved to be fruitful and started to penetrate into the cerebral mystery.

In order to do this, it was necessary to dare to apply the cellular conception to the nervous system. It was in this way that the notion of a nerve cell (neuron *) was arrived at and that it was possible to bring to light the inmost structure of these centers thanks to the researches of Golgi (1873) and especially of Ramon y Cajal (1894), the brilliant Spanish histologist who, toward the end of the century, explained the architecture of the brain. It was also necessary for the discoveries of Galvani (1788) and Matteucci (1842), who were both Italian, and of the German, Du Bois-Reymond (1848), to demonstrate the electrical nature of the

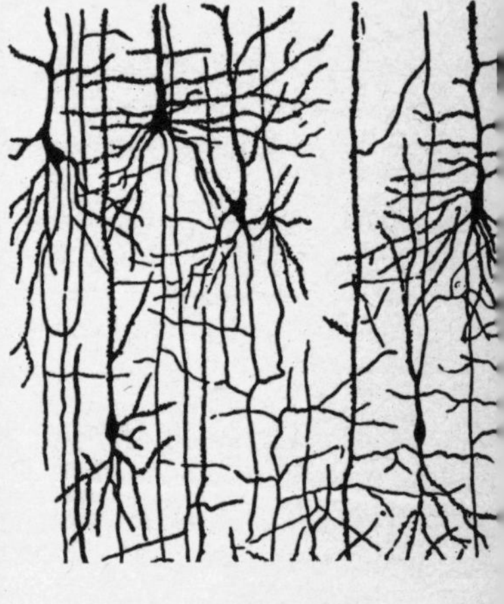

The explorer of the thinking network, th Spanish histologist Ramon y Cajal (1852-1934 Nobel prize 1906. Using silver stains, he analy ed the neuronic structure of the nerve center and the diagrams he made remain classic toda

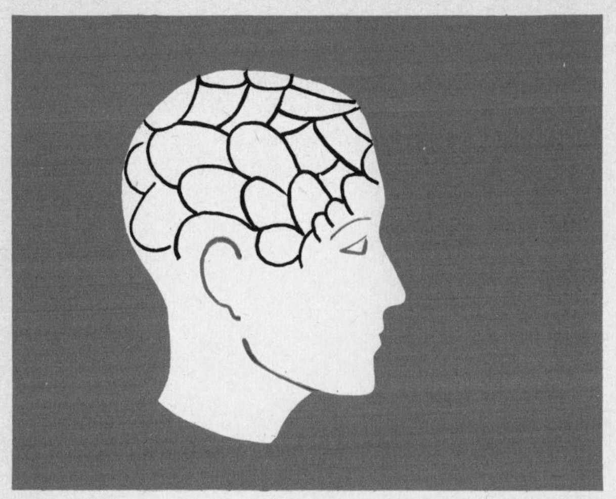

The whimsical cranial bumps of phrenology, the seats of psychic faculties.

nervous impulse.* The laws of the elementary reflexes had to be stated precisely as a result of Pflüger's experiments (1850). Above all, the characteristics of cerebral functioning had to be demonstrated by the synthesis of experimentation on animals' brains and observations of human patients whose lesions were subsequently revealed by autopsy.

The beginning of the nineteenth century saw the researcher Flourens, who used ablations of pigeons' brains to show the psychic role of that organ but concluded that it functions as a whole, confront Gall, a doctor and the founder of phrenology. Gall wanted to localize the various psychic functions in the various cerebral regions and sought to draw conclusions about them from the study of cranial bumps. While phrenology is false, there nonetheless exist *cerebral localizations,* * not of the psychism but of sensorial and motor functions. This had to be recognized after the observations of Broca (1861) on a patient to whom localized lesions gave linguistic difficulties and the experiments of Fritsch and Hitzig (1870), which revealed the existence of cerebral psychomotor centers. During the last years of the century much ingenuity was exercised in drawing a map of the brain in an attempt to find the seat of consciousness and volition, as well as storehouses of images, the props of memory. Attempts were made to discover the differences between the brains of great men and those of criminals. While these researches advanced our knowledge of the structures and functions of the various parts of the brain, they also showed the impossibility of localizing concretely in the brain anything of a higher psychological order.

Beginning with our century, cerebral neurophysiology also entered a new stage and became more objective, particularly under the impact of the great Russian neurophysiologist Pavlov. It limited itself to its proper area: the study of the cerebral nervous mechanisms of behavior. * It shunned any recourse to the vocabulary of psychology. No longer was it a question of trying to search for consciousness or volition in the brain, or of explaining reactions by referring to the subjectivity of the being who feels or wills, but of examining what was happening in the brain at one precise moment. While the work of Sherrington, Adrian, and L. Lapicque was increasing our knowledge of elemen-

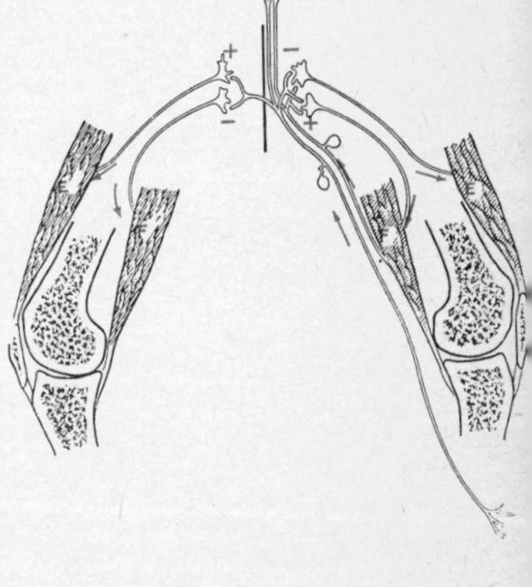

The physiologist who analyzed the reflex functioning of the spinal cord and revealed to us the innermost mechanisms of nervous functioning, the Englishman Sherrington (1857-1952). Nobel prize 1932. Author of two famous works. "The Integrative Action of the Nervous System" (1906) and "Man on his Nature" (1937). The diagram explains the reciprocal innervation of antagonistic muscles in the case of extending (E) and flexing (F) the leg.

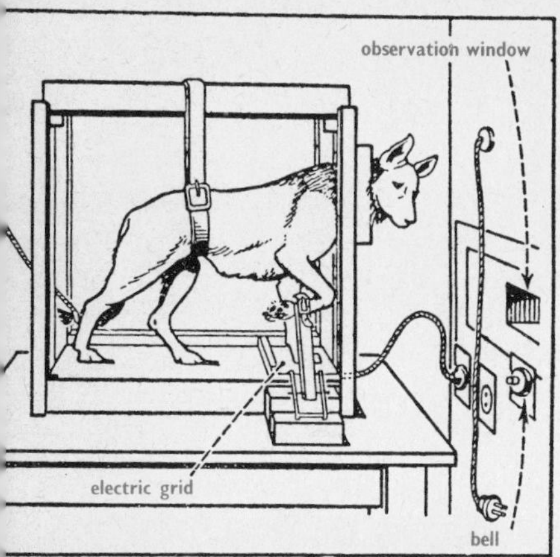

The master of the living brain, the Russian Pavlov (1849-1936). Nobel prize 1904. After studying salivary reflexes and gastric secretion, he used the old method of training in order to study from the outside what goes on in the brain. Author of "Lectures on Conditioned Reflexes," 2 vols (1928 and 1941). Above: diagram of a device for studying a dog's conditioned reflexes by the Pavlovian method (association of the electric excitant with a bell that sets off a bending of the paw).

tary nervous functioning, Pavlov was demonstrating that this elementary functioning was enough to ensure the highest human cerebral functions. At the same time, cerebral physiology was enriched by the whole contribution on the neurophysiology of sleep resulting from the work of Von Economo on sleeping sickness (1920) and the possibility of recording the electric activity of the brain. It was thus that *electroencephalography* * was born, following the work of the German psychiatrist H. Berger (1929).

Whereas Pavlov had deduced what was going on in the brain from a careful analysis of external behavior, it was becoming possible, thanks to technical progress, to study cerebral activity directly. It was no longer a matter of observing a few elementary reactions in an animal that had been deeply upset by a serious operation, but of recording the cerebral activity of a normal animal, in its ordinary living conditions, not at all disturbed by the presence of fine needles placed ahead of time in its brain. A psycho-

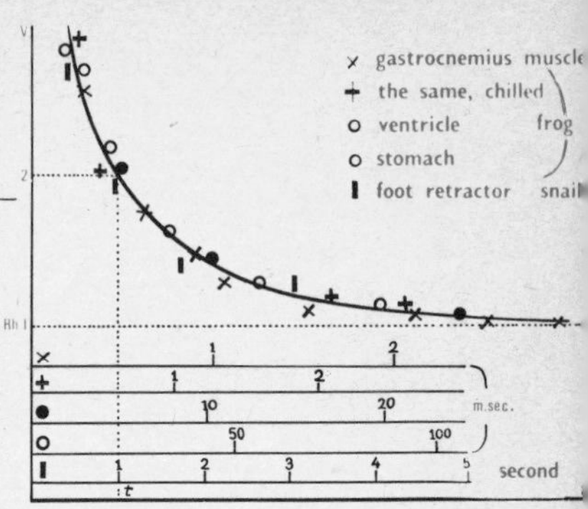

The father of "chronaxy," which made us understand the harmony of the nervous machine, the Frenchman L. Lapicque (1866-1952), who, in collaboration with his wife, used the test of electric excitability to discover the function of nervous regulation (subordination). He also investigated the relationship between brain weight and body weight. Author of "The Nervous Machine" (1942). The curve shows the laws of electric excitability of the various tissues. The scale of time values is different in each case.

logical neurophysiology, born in 1933 with the work of Fulton, has thus flourished during the last ten years. Psychism is still not found in the brain, nor is the brain explained by resorting to psychic terms, but progress has been such that the neurophysiologist can no longer neglect, for example, consciousness as an epiphenomenon. He can now specify its cerebral conditions. This is a new aspect that cannot be overlooked, although it has nothing to do with the specific dimension or the nature of consciousness, which will always remain a psychological or philosophic problem.

It is all the more impossible to neglect subjectivity in a modern study of the brain, which is the organ of that subjectivity, because experimental neurophysiology does not confine itself to the study of animals' brains. It has penetrated to the operating room of the neurosurgeon, who must understand the functioning of the human brain in order to heal it when sick. The painless character of operations on the brain frequently makes it possible to operate on a wide-awake subject, who thus contributes a precious, irreplaceable report on what he feels.

We may add that the *cybernetic* * point of view (Norbert Wiener, 1948) – that is, the comparison of the brain to great modern electronic machines – has turned out to be very fruitful. It has shown both what the brain and the machine have in common and what is peculiar to the brain.

For a long time it was possible for the neurophysiology of the brain to remain the concern of only a few specialists. Because of its spectacular progress, it gains daily in command, not just of technical skills and knowledge, but of the technique of cerebral manipulation, based upon an understanding of the organ which is responsible for what is specifically mental and spiritual in human life. Is it not henceforth indispensable for any cultivated person to have some knowledge of this field? And not out of mere curiosity: it offers, through understanding of oneself and others, the foundation of a *hygiene* * *of conduct*, of an art of being better and more complete men in a more human society. An indispensable art for modern man, if he wants to keep his destiny from falling into the hands of sorcerers' apprentices. A wisdom based upon the correct use of the human brain would be capable of making an objective contribution to traditional humanism, which has become so devaluated in our technical age.

It is in this spirit that we want to present the human brain. After examining the cerebral structures and the elementary mechanisms that govern their functions, we shall ask ourselves how all this can account for human psychism: thought, consciousness, and volition. We shall then examine the practical consequences of this knowledge, and all the possibilities of manipulating the brain for the healing of pathological disorders. We shall point out to what extent there are available in this field techniques capable of being used for good or for evil on a normal brain, and we shall indicate what should be done to have and to preserve a normal brain.

·I·VĒTRICVLVS
·II·VĒTRICVLVS
·III·VĒTRICVLVS

The Cerebral Organ

Geography of the brain

Our organism functions in a way that is adapted to its needs. On the one hand, as far as the activity of the various internal organs is concerned, we refer to the metabolic aspects: "life of *nutrition*" *; on the other hand, in the realm of the interaction of the organism with its external environment, we speak of its relational aspects: "life of *relation*." * In both cases, its functioning depends on its nerve centers,* which are organs of co-ordination and integration * and which, upon receiving informative sensory messages, send out action orders appropriate to the particular situation.

Local or regional regulatory action can be taken care of by lower centers such as the spinal cord or the sympathetic ganglia,* but the higher part of the nerve centers is the *encephalon,** which is located in the skull. Its functions include certain local regulatory actions (in the region of the head particularly) but above all a general control of the organism. Thanks to the encephalon, the billions of living cells which make up the organism become a superior unity, an individual, and, in the case of man, a conscious person. The encephalon weighs an average of 48 ounces (1360 grams) in men; it weighs somewhat less in women – 44 ounces (1220 grams) – because of their lighter average weight. This corresponds, in the case of a man, to 1/48 of the weight of his body. It is divided into a brain stem * or base of the brain * surmounted at its top by the *brain*

The lakes of the brain, the ventricles (sixteenth century).

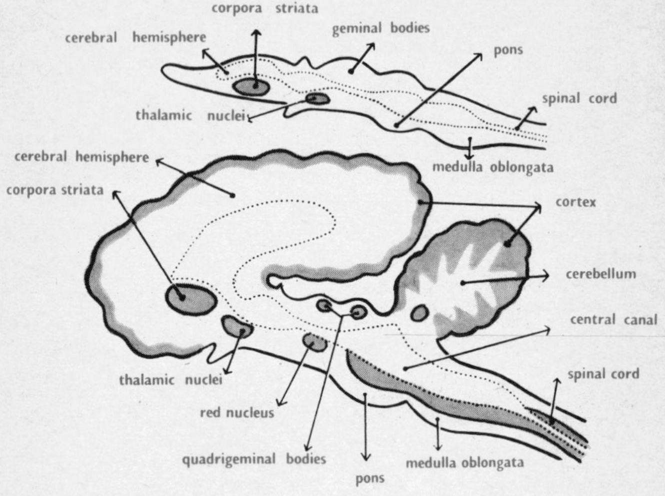

The various centers of the encephalon, in a fish (above) and in man (below).

proper and behind it by the *cerebellum.** It includes a whole hierarchy of nerve centers. Most of them are automatic centers involving neither consciousness nor volition. Among these, in the lower part that prolongs the spinal cord, are the *medulla oblongata* * and the *pons,** which coordinate the activity of the various organs, ensure automatic breathing, and use messages from the various senses, particularly the sense of balance originating in the inner ear, in order to regulate the degree of contraction of the various muscles upon which attitudes and movements depend *(muscular tonus *).* These centers are normally the object of a precise control that depends partly on the next higher level, the midbrain, cerebral *isthmus,* * or *mesencephalon,* * of which the upper portion forms the two pairs of *corpora quadrigemina* * and the basal portion forms the *cerebral peduncles* * (which are thick bundles of white matter with the *red nucleus* * at their center), and partly on the *cerebellum,* which is located further back. But the initiation of bodily movements and of varied kinds of behavior in the outside environment is taken care of by the upper part of the encephalon, the only part that is visible when the top of the skull is opened. These *cerebral hemispheres* * constitute the brain proper, the most highly developed part of man's encephalon, the organ of psychism, consciousness, and volition. Through them, we are conscious of ourselves, we can become conscious of the outside world and of other people, we can perform certain acts in a deliberate way, we remember and we imagine. Their functioning provides not only our psychological life but also the course of our thinking, the consciousness we have of it, and the possibility of directing it.

Whereas the medulla oblongata, the pons, and the mesencephalon form a single mass, we have two cerebral hemispheres, one on the right and one on the left. Because of the organization of most of the paths of sensitivity and

Man's encephalon seen from below.

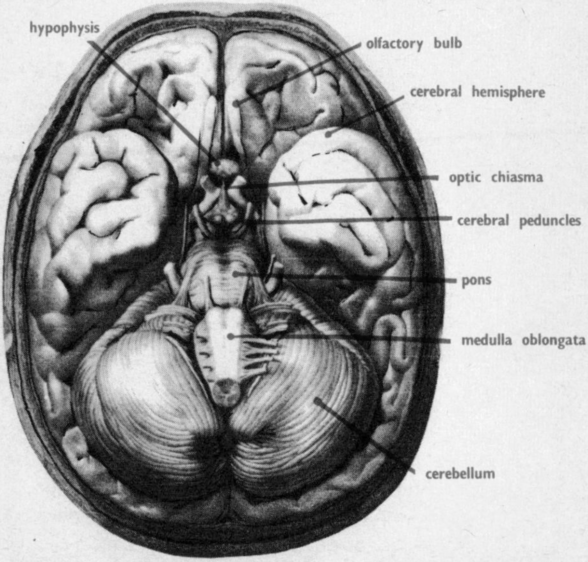

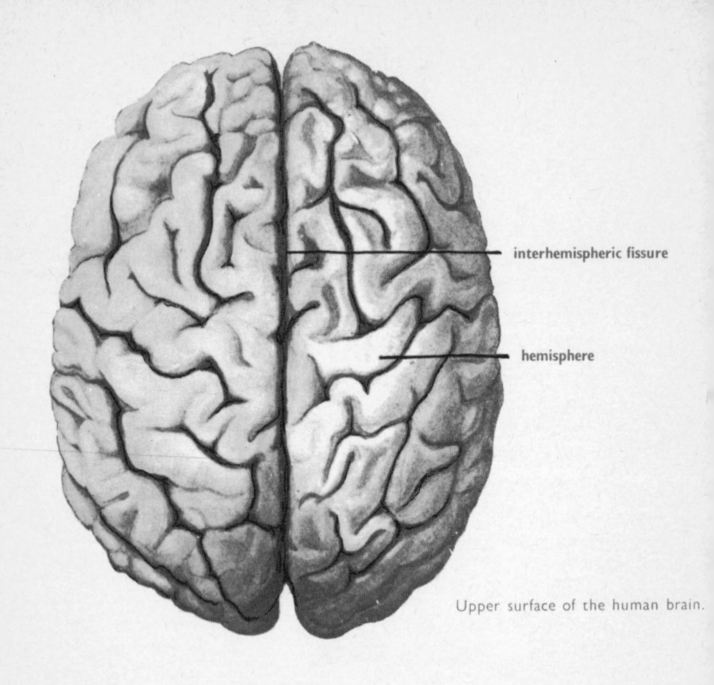

Upper surface of the human brain.

motoricity, which are crossed, we can say that the right hemisphere concerns particularly the left side of the body, and the left hemisphere the right side. The two hemispheres are not independent. They are connected at their base, for one thing; and, for another, thick bundles of fibers, the main one being the *corpus callosum,** unite their inside surfaces, so that they function in a co-ordinated way. Like all nerve centers, the hemispheres include zones of white matter * – that is, nerve fibers providing connections between the various parts – and zones of gray matter,* which are the region of nerve cells, of their processes and their innumerable contacts – in brief, the inextricable network upon which the brain's functions depend. In this way we distinguish the *cerebral cortex,** the outer gray layer, two or three millimeters thick, which surrounds the whole hemisphere on its outer surface, its upper and lower parts, and at the top and bottom of its inside surface. Underneath this gray layer, there is an important white zone. Finally,

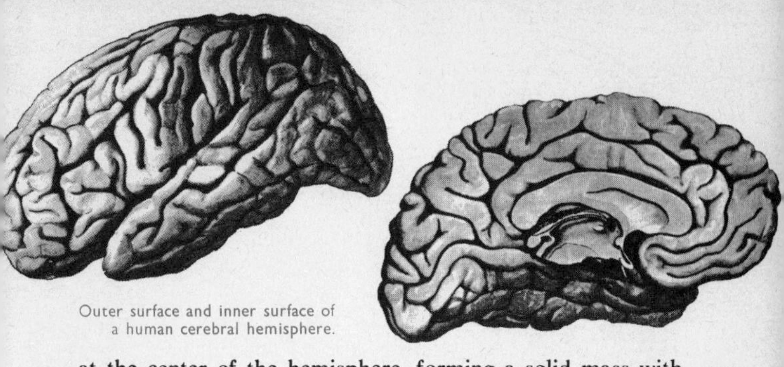

Outer surface and inner surface of a human cerebral hemisphere.

at the center of the hemisphere, forming a solid mass with the opposite side and joining the hemisphere to the mesencephalon, are the *central gray nuclei* * or basal ganglia of the brain, with various bundles of white matter between them connecting the brain with the rest of the encephalon. Like the other parts of the encephalon, the hemispheres have a cavity inside, the *lateral ventricle.* Between the central gray nuclei, the right and left lateral ventricles communicate with a single central cavity, called the *third ventricle,* which opens behind into the *aqueduct of Sylvius,* the narrow cavity of the mesencephalon. The ventricles are filled with cerebrospinal fluid, as are the meningeal spaces located in the *meninges* * surrounding the encephalon.

The cerebral cortex and the central gray nuclei function together as a unit, and are responsible for behavior and psychism. But the importance of the cortex is predominant. Its organization is the more complex: it includes fourteen billion cells, manifoldly interconnected - in others words,

Diagram: RO - fissure of Rolando. SY - fissure of Sylvius. Pe - perpendicular fissure. Cal - calcarine fissure. F - frontal lobe. PF - prefrontal zone. SO - orbital region. Fa - frontal region next to fissure of Rolando. Pa - parietal lobe. Paa - parietal region next to fissure of Rolando. PC - curved fold. LPC - paracentral lobule. T - temporal lobe. O - occipital lobe. Cu - cuneus. CIN - cingulum. CH - convolution of the hippocampus. CC - corpus callosum. Tr - trigone.

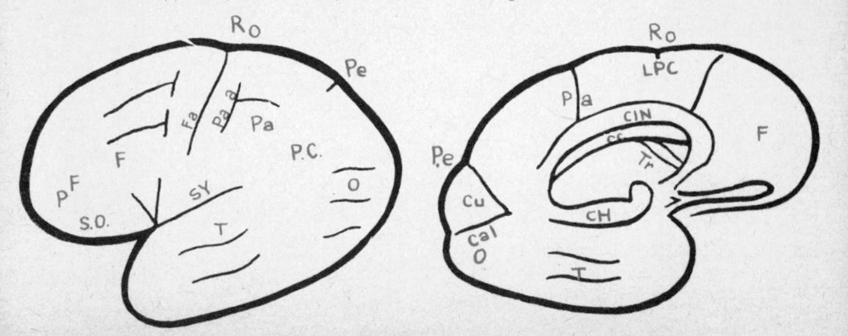

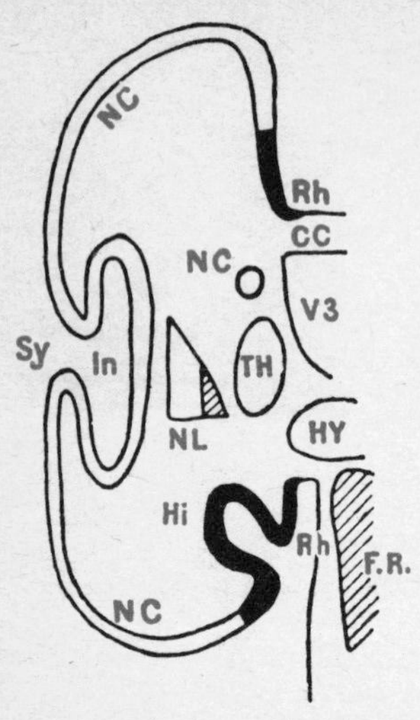

The centers of behavior. Vertical cross section of the brain. On the surface: Rh - rhinencephalon. NC - neo cortex. Sy - fissure of Sylvius. In - insular lobe. Beneath the surface, the central gray nuclei. Th - thalamus. NC - caudate nucleus. NL - lenticular nucleus. V3 - third ventricle. CC - corpus callosum. Hy - hypothalamus. FR - reticular formation. Hi - hippocampus.

the acme of complexity in living matter, far surpassing the modest achievements of our calculating machines. Although the nerve circuits of the cortex cannot function independently of their relationship with the basal ganglia, they are nonetheless the elective seat of nervous phenomena, the basis of psychic life. Not all these phenomena are conscious, just as not all the orders coming from the cortex are volitional, but it is in the cortex that consciousness and volition are born. There can be no life of the mind without a cerebral cortex in good condition. It is the essential human organ.

As for the basal ganglia, they have a share in the proper functioning of the cortex and, in conjunction with it, are responsible for numerous behavioral automatisms, particularly in the instinctive and affective area. They play a role that is important for the psychism and have repercussions upon it, but in an indirect way, through their relationship with the cortex. Three groups of basal ganglia may be distinguished: on each side of the third ventricle are the *corpora striata,** which are centers of motor automatisms, and the *thalami,** sensitive and sensorial reception centers and co-ordinating centers of the cortex. Under the third ventricle is the single mass of nuclei called the *hypothalamus,* * which is the center of the unconscious automatisms of the instincts and of affectivity. The hypothalamus is in close relationship with the hypophysis,* or pituitary gland, which hangs beneath it. The thalamus, hypothalamus, and third ventricle make up the *diencephalon,** as opposed to the corpora striata and the cerebral cortex *(telencephalon *).*

The cerebral cortex is not smooth but has numerous clefts, grooves, or fissures * marking off convolutions in such a way that the total surface area of the two hemispheres is, surprisingly, about 300 square inches. Especially important are the *central fissure of Rolando* on the upper part of the outer surface and the *Sylvian fissure* on the lower part. They make it possible to distinguish various regions of the cortex called *lobes.* * The anterior part of the cortex, in front of the central fissure, is the *frontal lobe,* which includes an outer surface, an under surface located above the ocular orbit, and an inner surface. Behind and above the central fissure is the *parietal lobe.* Below the Sylvian fissure is the *temporal lobe.* The posterior portion of the hemisphere constitutes the *occipital lobe.* There exists a lobe hidden deeply within the Sylvian fissure, called the *insular lobe.* Finally, at the center of the inner surface, separated by a fissure from the other lobes and rolled like

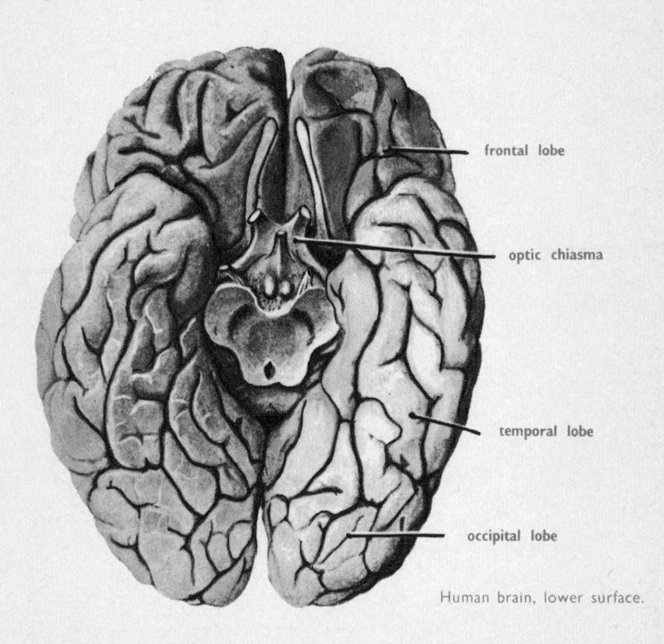

Human brain, lower surface.

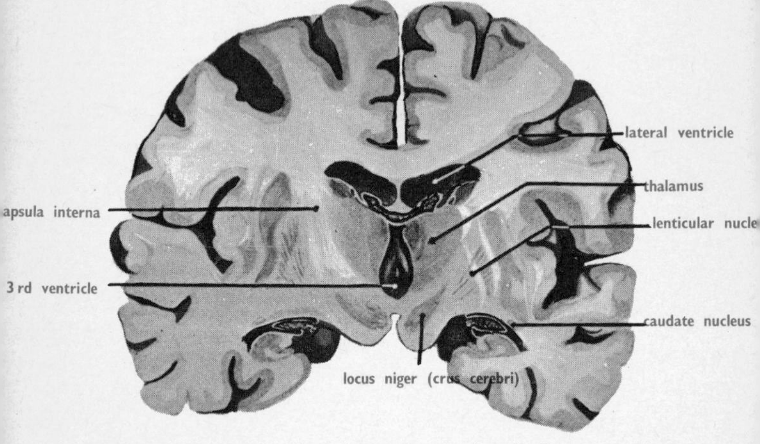

Vertical cross section of the brain showing the central ganglia. Compare with the drawing on p. 20

a ring around the central gray nuclei, above and below them, is the most primitive and least differentiated part of the cortex, the *primitive brain* or *rhinencephalon.** It is in contrast to this that the rest of the cortex is called *neocortex.**

Innumerable secondary grooves make it possible to distinguish in each lobe numerous convolutions that are described and numbered in atlases of the brain. Only a few have a distinct function.

Of the twelve pairs of cranial nerves * that originate in the encephalon, two are connected to the cerebral hemispheres. Actually, they are not so much nerves as true extensions of the brain. Beginning at the rear of the thalamus are *optic tracts* which go around the encephalon and unite in front of the hypophysis in an *optic chiasma.** From this starting point, the two optic nerves terminate in the retinas of the eyes. The *olfactory tract* begins in the rhinencephalon and terminates in the *olfactory bulb,* a nerve center located under the hemisphere and receiving the olfactory fibers coming from the nasal olfactory organ.

Each cerebral lobe has its own physiological role, while all of them collaborate in our psychic life. The primitive brain is first of all, by virtue of its relationship with our olfactory equipment, an olfactory brain, and that is why it is called the rhinencephalon (Gr. *rhis* = nose, and *enkephalos* = brain); but it is very complicated and, in man, its olfactory function is limited when compared to its role in the automatisms of instinct and affectivity. Modern neurosurgery * presupposes a knowledge of certain of its parts that the nonspecialist does not have to know how to locate exactly: cingulum, hippocampus, etc.

The parietal lobe is the brain of general sensitivity, such as that of the skin, the muscles, the joints, etc. The temporal lobe is the auditory brain. The occipital lobe is the visual brain. As for the frontal lobe, it can be divided into three parts: the posterior part of its outer surface and of the upper zones of its inner surface is a psychomotor brain at the command of the will; its lower surface and the rest of its inner surface are annexed to the rhinencephalon; and its

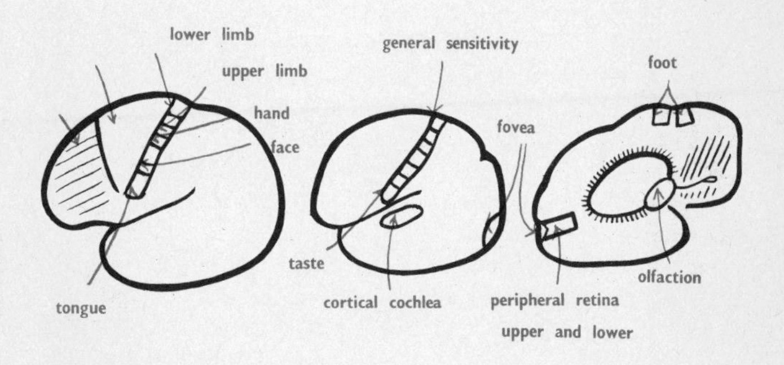

The cerebral localizations. First drawing on the left, motor localizations of the outer surface: motor area of the frontal region with the various zones of the body. Apm - premotor area. Pf - prefrontal zone of self-control Middle drawing, sensorial localizations of the outer surface: general sensitivity of the various zones of the body in the parietal region. Cortical cochlea (auditory) and cortical fovea (vision). On the right, inner surface: motor and sensory localizations of the foot, consisting of extensions of the frontal and the parietal regions. Peripheral retina. Olfactory zone and instinctive brain (shaded).

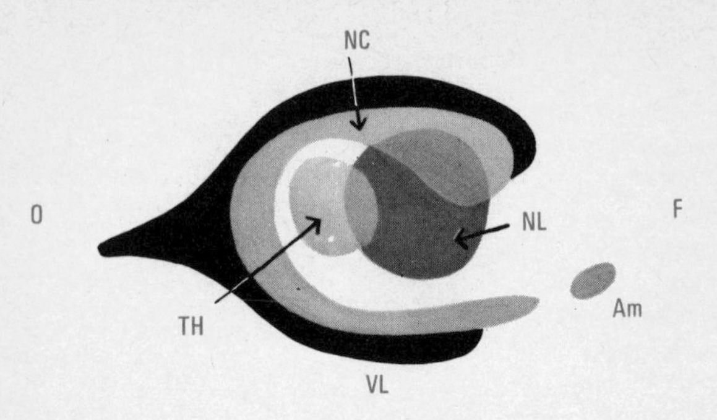

The central gray nuclei, side view. In black, the lateral ventricle VL. TH - thalamus. NL - lenticular nucleus. NC - caudate nucleus. Am - nucleus amygdalae. F - frontal region. O - occipital region.

anterior part, especially on its outer surface, is the most important zone of the human brain (prefrontal region *) – we shall learn how to locate in it the cerebral mechanisms that govern self-control.

The various regions of the cortex are associated with one another in three ways: by the uninterrupted continuity of the gray matter, by the intermediation of white matter, or by connections that are relayed deep within the central gray nuclei. This explains how the various zones of the cortex are related to various parts of the thalamus, which it has been possible to locate precisely.

The cavity within each hemisphere, the lateral ventricle, is extended by a frontal, a temporal, and an occipital prolongation. The massive shape of the thalamus and of the central part of the corpus striatum called the *lenticular nucleus* forms a contrast to the coiled appearance of its outer part, the *caudate nucleus*, with its swollen frontal head, posterior body, and tapering temporal tail.

Thus, briefly described, is the human brain. Centuries of exploration – empirical at first, then more and more methodical – have made it possible to draw up a more precise map of it than the ones we possess of most of the lands on our planet. Physicians, biologists, surgeons, and all the specialists in neurology have contributed toward tracking down and localizing the mystery of our brain.

Man without his brain

Is the brain the organ of thought, of intelligence, of volition – in short, of the life of the mind and spirit? Experimentation on man would give us irrefutable proof of this. However, it seems difficult – even under the pretext of legitimate scientific curiosity – to remove an individual's brain. But certain accidents that deprive man either wholly or partially of the use of his brain provide us with a proof by the *reductio ad absurdum* method. Whether the brain is completely destroyed, or merely suffering from severe shock and incapable of functioning, man is in a *coma,** without consciousness or volition. He can still live if the lower centers of the medulla continue to function, but his mental life is either suspended, if the brain is capable of being repaired, or permanently abolished. He then goes on in a vegetative existence that no longer has anything human about it.

Although it is protected by multiple natural defenses, notably the skull and the hydraulic protection afforded by the cerebrospinal fluid,* our brain is very fragile and very vulnerable. The causes of coma are accordingly innumerable. In addition to cerebral damage, a violent blow on the head causes the kind of coma called syncope. If the contusion, although not serious enough to bring on a coma, has caused an intracranial hemorrhage, the brain, as a result of being squeezed in this unexpandable cavity, suffers and stops functioning. The same thing is true if the compression is due to an excess of cerebrospinal fluid or to the excessive growth of an intracranial tumor. Experimentally in neurosurgery, and more easily in the case of animals, the brain can be stopped by being compressed; the subject can thus be made to lose consciousness whenever this is desired.

The brain is made up of living cells that have very substantial requirements, as we shall see later on, in the form of oxygen and sugar. The replenishment is taken care of by a rich irrigation of blood. Any disturbance in this area upsets and then stops cerebral functioning, for there is a rigorous parallelism between cerebral suffering and psychic disturbances. Coma caused by serious circulatory disorders such as a cerebral hemorrhage or a spasm which obliterates the cerebral vessels, a clot or air bubble which obstructs them, coma of an aviator subjected to strong accelerations that disturb cerebral circulation, coma caused by serious general hemorrhages or by cardiac syncopes – if the circulation stops during a few seconds for any of these reasons, the cerebral cortex ceases to function, and if the disturbance lasts several minutes, permanent damage will be caused. Thus after an excessively prolonged operative syncope, a lesion of the occipital brain may result in permanent blindness. The same is true if the syncope is respiratory, if the cessation of breathing prevents oxygenation of the brain, or if the surrounding atmosphere, as at high altitudes, becomes unfit for breathing; without an oxygen mask, a coma would result. The same is also true if the blood cannot carry the oxygen, as in the case of poisoning by carbon monoxide. Every serious disturbance in cerebral alimentation will produce the same result, whether it be a lack of glucose in the case of insulin coma or poisoning in diabetic or uremic comas.

Because of its sensitivity, the brain is very often the first organ to suffer from disturbances of the organism. Besides

Effect on a monkey of increasing accelerations in the head-to-seat direction (from 0 to 7.7 times the normal weight of gravity). Notice the flattening of the heart as it is emptied of blood, causing disturbance of cerebral circulation.

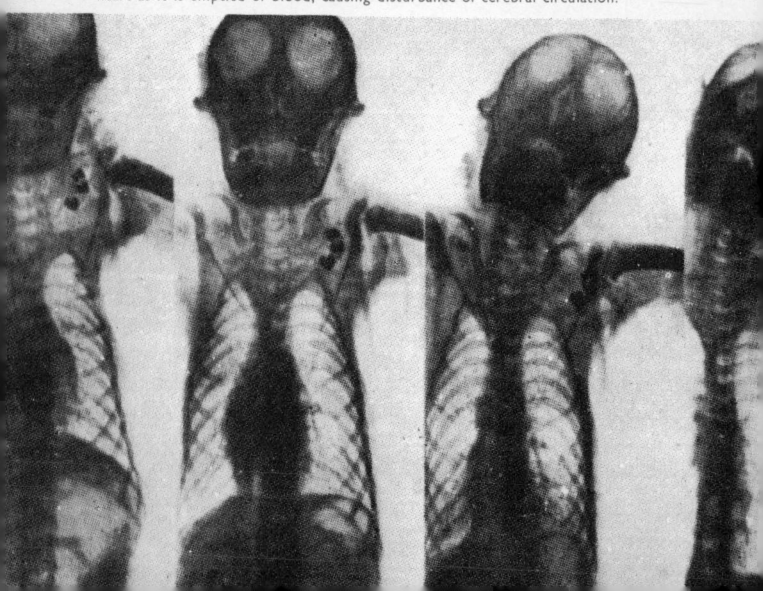

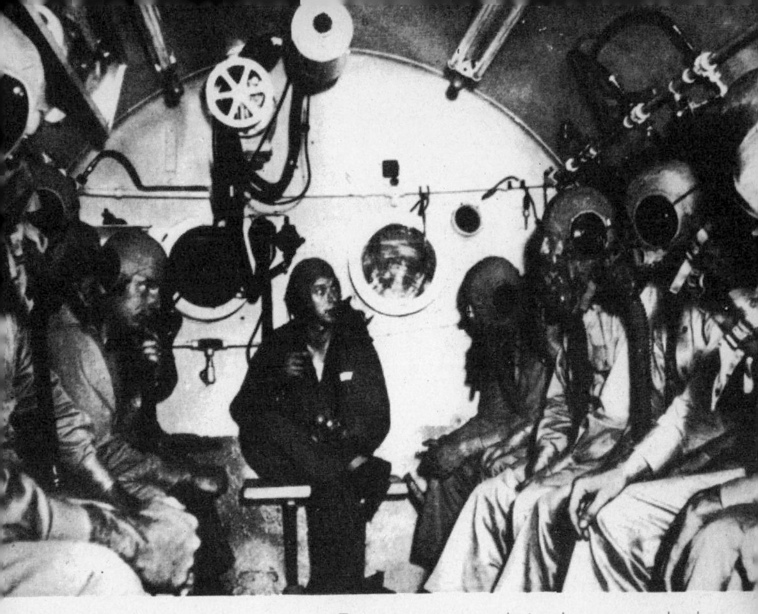

Trying out oxygen masks in a low-pressure chamber.

the chemical factors, there are the physical factors. Our brain is used to the normal temperature of 98.6 degrees F. An excess of fever causes delirium, and hypothermia (low temperature) leads to a coma.

Every time a man loses consciousness, his brain may be observed to be in poor condition, whether its impairment is direct or is a secondary result of the poor condition of the organism. Correcting the disturbance, when this is possible, restores consciousness if the brain can resume its normal functioning. But in addition to serious, generalized disturbances, which result in coma, any slighter or more localized impairment of cerebral functioning will be revealed by psychic symptoms. We know today that many of the faults of children, such as laziness, bad temper, and aggressiveness, depend on humoral disturbances arising from states of disequilibrium in the endocrine glands,* which produce *hormones* * that affect the brain. An aviator who rises to high altitudes or goes into a low-pressure chamber

without a mask and a swimmer wearing a diving suit provided with compressed air or oxygen who descends too far will manifest various serious psychic disturbances – slowed reactions, poor judgment, mistakes in reckoning and spelling, etc. – which may lead them to make fatal decisions, all because their brains lack oxygen or are poisoned by oxygen or nitrogen under pressure. Let us also point out the importance of *vitamins.**

The numerous chemical substances which, being endowed with the power to act on the psychism, can be used as medicines are brain poisons whose mode of action is being revealed to us more and more by modern experimentation. Some of them slow down cerebral activity, calming agitation, leading to sleep or, in the case of others, to *narcosis* * – actually a controllable coma – by general anesthetics,* which are so useful in surgery. Others are excitants. There are some whose action is more elective and provokes hallu-

Human centrifuge for the selection of aviators and rocket pilots; resistance to acceleration. French headquarters at Brétigny.

cinations * and real mental disorders. Although we are still far from knowing exactly which cerebral perturbations are responsible for psychiatric disorders, it is certain that these mental illnesses, even if they are not accompanied by visible lesions of the brain, are the result of that organ's functioning poorly. During neurosurgical operations it is possible, either by localized destructions for therapeutic purposes or by excitations, to act in a selective way upon the psychism. Such procedures offer obvious proof of the connection between the psychism and the brain. Hallucinations can be caused, sleep induced, memories recalled, speech made impossible, character and disposition modified. The various aspects of mental activity are accompanied by specific modifications of cerebral activity in its totality or in certain regions. What is sleep if not a natural, periodic loss of consciousness? It is just that: rest for the brain, whose activity is profoundly slowed down and loses its regulatory action. The characteristics of the sleeping brain explain the incoherence of dreams.

It has been possible to remove portions of the brain by surgery without affecting consciousness and psychism. Depending on the zone, only motor or sensory disturbances are caused. It has even been possible, when there has been a lesion, to removc an entire hemisphere without disturbing the psychism; but it must be the right one (the one which controls the left hand of a right-handed person and does not include the language centers). This does not mean that this hemisphere was useless, but that our psychism is not rigorously localized in our brain and that the remaining parts make up for the missing ones.

Of course, there can be no question of experimentally removing a man's brain. But because of what pathology teaches us, we know without doing so that this would mean plunging him into a coma. For that matter, developmental disturbances sometimes bring into being a monster born without a brain *(anencephalus *)*. Such creatures have lived long enough for us to observe the absence of development in either their psychism or their consciousness. At other times a less severe disturbance produces a child with an abnormal brain whose psychism will be very limited. Such, for example, are the victims of hydrocephalus,* whose skulls are swollen by an accumulation of cerebrospinal fluid press-

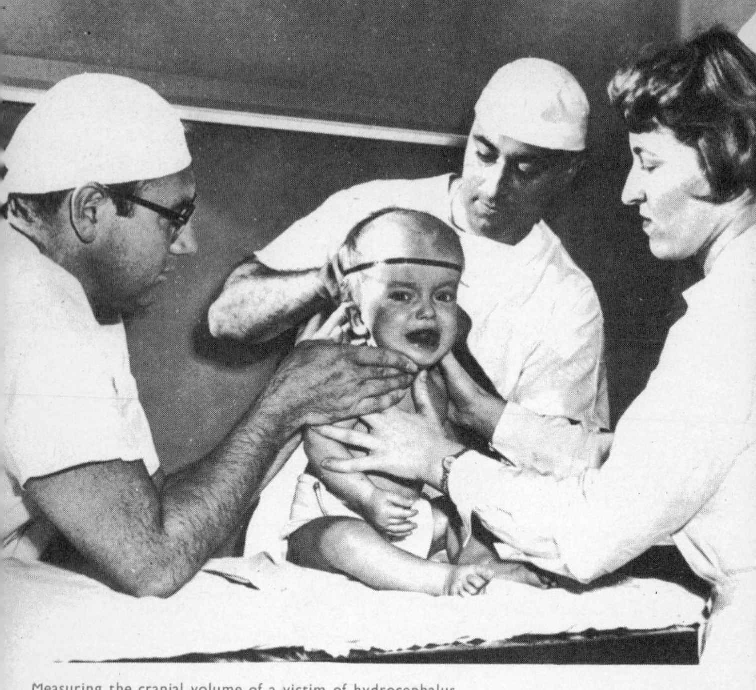

Measuring the cranial volume of a victim of hydrocephalus.

ing upon the brain, or children who have had a thyroid deficiency before birth and whose brains have developed poorly. Both kinds of children are condemned to mental debility.

Finally, by experimenting on animals, we can easily observe the influence of all the preceding factors and even of ablation of the brain. Animal psychology is well enough developed today to make it possible to judge degrees of intelligence objectively from various kinds of behavior. Flourens, who was the first to perform an ablation of the brain of a pigeon, observed its impenetrable torpor. An animal without a cerebellum merely has difficulty in keeping its balance, whereas an animal without a brain no longer has any psychism.

More interesting are operations performed on creatures that are more like us, such as dogs (Goltz, 1899; Rothmann, 1909) or monkeys. If the entire brain is removed, the animal is in a coma and loses all initiative; only elementary reflexes remain. On the other hand, if the basal ganglia are left intact, a great difference may be observed between a dog and a monkey. The monkey, like a man with a serious cerebral lesion, is in a coma and loses all intelligence. The dog, on the contrary, seems normal at first glance: it walks, avoids obstacles, eats if food is placed right under its nose, and shows its pleasure or anger in an exaggerated way. Actually, a closer analysis reveals, it has become a kind of automaton whose activity lacks all the delicate nuances that make it possible to speak of intelligence. It has lost all the habits acquired through training and cannot adapt its behavior to the situation. It could not live outside the protected world of the laboratory. We must therefore distinguish two levels in its activity: an automatic elementary level governed by the central gray nuclei, and a higher psychic level that requires the cerebral cortex. The same is true of monkeys and men, but in their case the automatic activity of the central gray nuclei can take place only where there is a much more highly developed cerebral cortex which has taken charge of certain essential functions.

Conversely, the further one goes down the scale of animals, the less important becomes the cerebral cortex; psychic functions, which are increasingly limited, are then taken care of by the lower centers – the central gray nuclei or even the mesencephalon. Indeed, only mammals possess a well-developed cerebral cortex, a neocortex. In birds the cortex is small and the corpus striatum gigantic. In reptiles, batrachians, and fish, the cortex is absent, the hemispheres consisting of no more than the basal nuclei and the olfactory brain; their ablation modifies behavior very little. Even in invertebrates, whose ganglionic nervous system is very different from ours, psychic functions depend on the ganglia of the head, called *cerebroid ganglia,* which are the equivalent of our brain.

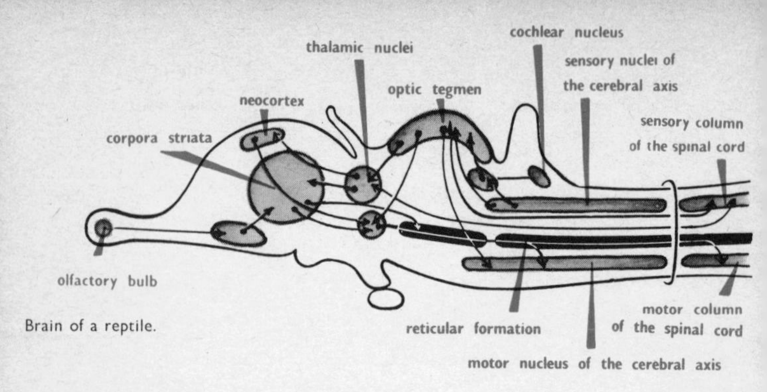

Brain of a reptile.

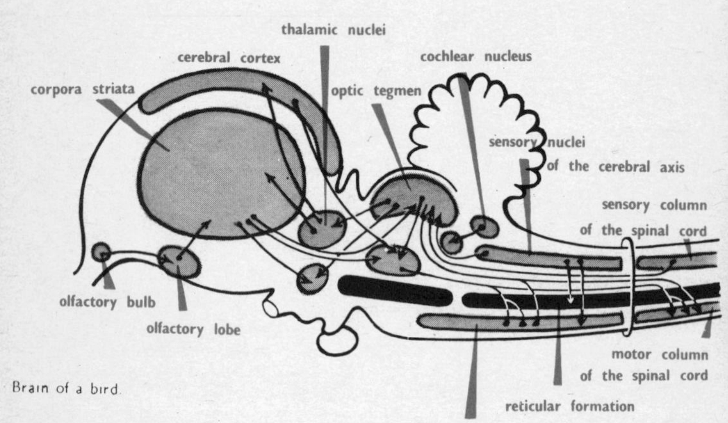

Brain of a bird.

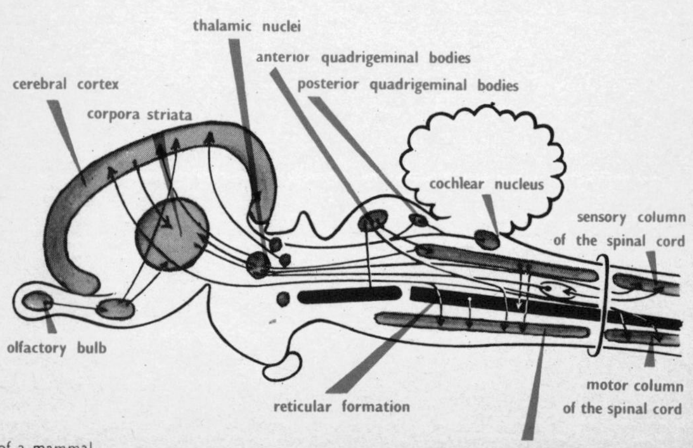

Brain of a mammal.

From animal to man

For the biologist, man is not a creature entirely apart. He has his place in the animal scale: he is a mammal, a primate, * placed by zoology in proximity to the higher monkeys, the anthropoids, * such as the chimpanzee. But then what about the superiority he has claimed for himself? Is it childish pride? Not at all. Modern comparative psychology shows us that it is indeed man that possesses the most complex psychism. Other animals have more highly developed instincts, and from this point of view man is backward, but nature compensates for the deficiency of instinct in him by the development of intelligence and the power of reflection. He can thus adopt the wisest and most appropriate conduct; on the other hand, he also possesses a much greater aptitude for losing his equilibrium. To anyone who makes an objective comparison of the potentialities of chimpanzees and men, there can be no question that, if the former possess a certain practical intelligence, the latter are so superior that their psychic nature seems to be of a different order. Are we to conclude therefore that this superiority of the human psychism is purely metaphysical, that it comes from the "soul" and not from the "body"?

The modern neurophysiologist must affirm that even in terms of his body – that is, in the biological aspect of his being – man is superior. This biological superiority is primarily of a cultural nature. Modern man is civilized; that is, unlike the chimpanzee, he has taken advantage of the acquisitions of preceding generations and has progressed unceasingly. There are animals that are better equipped for running and for hunting, and that have certain organs infinitely more complex than man's. Among mammals, man is a fairly primitive creature, rather slightly differentiated, slightly adapted; we have only to look at his dentition, which is that of an omnivore, and his limbs, which are those of a plantigrade. What constitutes the organic superiority of man is his *brain*. He is the animal with the most complex brain. Now, it would be absurd to assign the same importance to the complexity of just any organ, which is

Development of the brain, from reptile to bird to mammal. Notice the limited neocortex of the reptile, the huge corpora striata of the bird, and the highly developed cerebral cortex of the mammal.

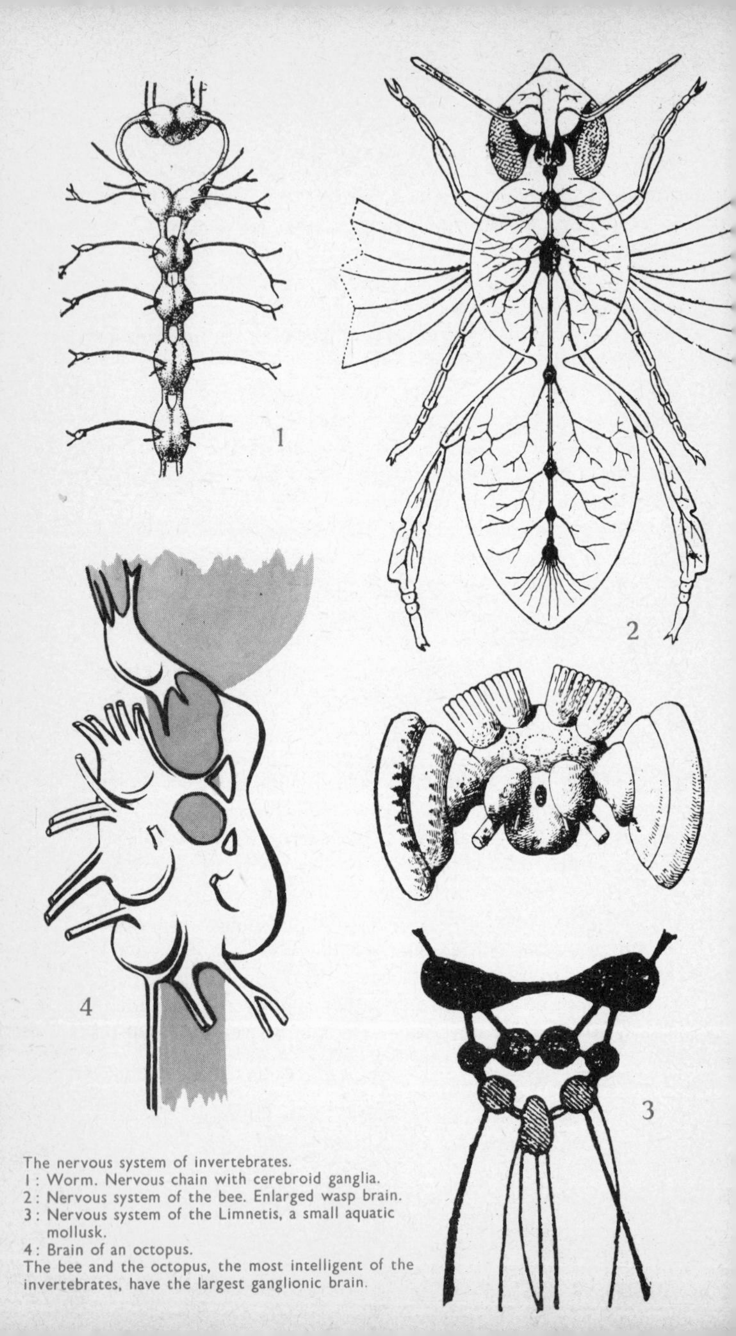

The nervous system of invertebrates.
1: Worm. Nervous chain with cerebroid ganglia.
2: Nervous system of the bee. Enlarged wasp brain.
3: Nervous system of the Limnetis, a small aquatic mollusk.
4: Brain of an octopus.
The bee and the octopus, the most intelligent of the invertebrates, have the largest ganglionic brain.

really a specialized tool, and the complexity of the brain, which is the origin of behavior adapted to various circumstances. Man has no wings, but he invents the rocket. It is the brain that makes possible cultural progress, which does not exist in the other social animals.

In the animal scale – and this is another proof of the role of the brain – it is possible to trace a parallel between the development of the brain (or more precisely of the higher nerve centers) and that of the psychism. However complex it may be, the behavior of a unicellular creature, such as an amoeba or infusorian, possessing no nervous system, is actually an *inferior psychism* and remains limited. It is only with the appearance of cerebroid ganglia in worms that an instinctive activity shows up. The acme of psychism in invertebrates is found in the bee and the octopus, whose cerebroid ganglia are the most important. In the scale of vertebrates, fish and batrachians that have no cerebral cortex remain at a level close to the preceding one. Intelligence is developed only in birds and mammals, and in the latter the maximum is attained by primates with the biggest brains. Finally, in the group of primates, an undeniable progression may be observed from the lower monkeys to the anthropoids and man. Here also the brain grows in importance, not only in its totality but particularly in its prefrontal part. This zone, which is only slightly developed in other mammals, represents 8 per cent of the cortex in lower monkeys, 12 per cent in ordinary monkeys, 17 per cent in chimpanzees, and 29 per cent in men.

To say that man is the living being whose brain is the most highly developed, in order to provide for his mental and reflective psychism, does not mean that he has the heaviest brain. It is the largest animals that have the heaviest brains: a whale's brain weighs more than thirteen pounds. Even if we take the relative weight of the brain by comparison with that of the body, we do not obtain a satisfactory relationship, for we find a higher ratio in small animals. The brain represents 1/500 of the body of a lion and 1/100 of a cat's, though both animals are of similar intelligence. Judging by relative weight, the mouse and the marmoset seem to be better equipped than man. This is because the brain grows less quickly than the body. The mathematical ratio between these two sizes, studied by the

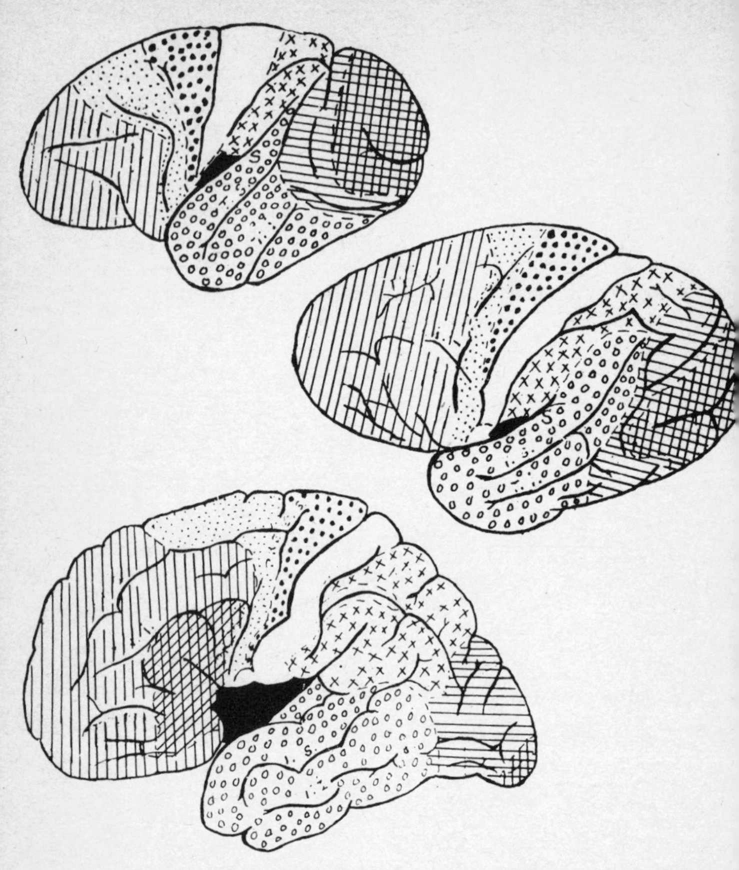

The progress of the brain from monkey to man, with the anthropoid in betwee

Dutchman E. Dubois (the discoverer of the Pithecanthropus) and by L. Lapicque, leads to obtaining a *coefficient of cephalization* * which objectifies the cerebral level of each species and makes it possible to situate the various animals on parallel lines whose position indicates both their degree of cerebralization and their intelligence. Man, whose coefficient is 2.73, appears above anthropoids (0.8), monkeys and carnivores (0.4), rabbits (0.18), and rats (0.08).

In any case, all this is valid only as a first approximation, because what is important for intelligence is not the weight

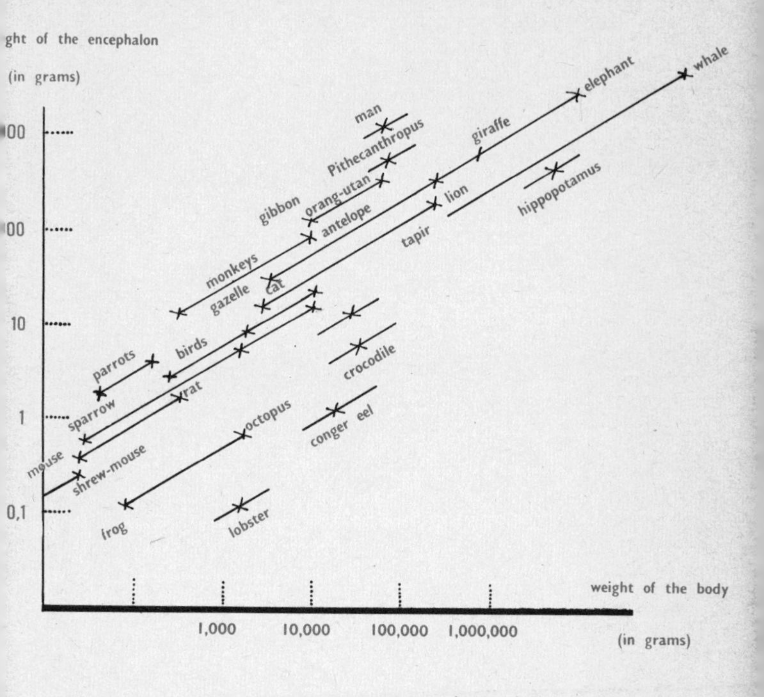

Lapicque's chart of cephalization.

of the brain or its volume, but its degree of complexity, which corresponds to the number of cells it is made up of and is only roughly proportional to its weight. In practice additional factors may intervene and qualify the consideration of weight as an indication of intellectual capabilities: the weight of the neurons and of their sheaths, the weight of the neuroglia,* the relative importance of the white matter, which is merely a conductor, and the gray matter, which is responsible for the psychism, as well as the relative importance of the reception and action centers as compared to the association centers. Finally, intellectual capacities depend on the richness of the cortical interconnections forming the nervous network of thought, a network that is all the denser the more cerebral nerve cells there are. Unfortunately, we still lack precise specifications in this area. Although mere brain weight is enough to indicate man's level by comparison with the chimpanzee's, it will not permit any conclusions in a comparison between individuals. Certain geniuses have lighter brains than some idiots. Moreover, one must take into consideration not merely the anatomical cerebral network but also its functional aptitudes.

Speaking very approximately, it may be said that improvement in the scale of primates consists of an increase in the number of neurons. Man has about four times as many neurons as a chimpanzee. This may not seem like much, but when one stops to think that man has 14 billion interconnected neurons and that the interconnections grow much more quickly than the number of elements, one realizes that the difference between man and monkey is, in the end, considerable and that it introduces into functional possibilities a genuine difference of kind. This is what explains how brains which seem to resemble each other closely are endowed with very different psychic powers.

Indeed, the comparison of a chimpanzee's brain with a man's reveals only slight differences anatomically; the former is merely somewhat smaller in all of its parts, especially the prefrontal. If we were dealing with just any organ, nothing important would result from this; but the case is quite different for an interconnected structure. Fewer elements in each zone will mean a slighter aptitude for perceiving and gesticulating, a slighter aptitude for syntheses, which are the foundation of thought. As we shall see, our inner language, which is the human modality of thought, depends on cerebral complexity, which is lacking in monkeys, who do not possess enough neurons to go beyond an animal's rudimentary thought and consciousness. Thus human superiority is observable not only by the psychologist and the philosopher, but can be recognized in its cerebral aspect by the neurophysiologist as well.

History of the brain

Man is not only the animal with the most complex brain; he is also the end result of an increase in cerebral *complexification.* * The various states of cerebral development that nature shows us today are not a mere curiosity but are the modern outcome of an ancient history. However incomplete the materials concerning the history of life and the animals of former times may be, we still know enough about them to affirm that it is not a history of incoherent, meaningless proliferation of varied species. There is an *evolution* of life as it transforms itself; species disappear and others replace them. Now, although in their details many changes seem to be meaningless or represent merely a better adaptation to a given environment, anyone who looks at evolution as a whole will see it as a true increase in complexity. The history of life offers us not only the complication of certain organs, but a great, significant, and constant improvement of the living being, which has become more and more unified and integrated as a result of the progress of its nervous structures and particularly of its brain. As time goes by, there appear in all groups species with increased cerebral activity; and, on the whole, the succession of animals is in the line of cerebral progress. In all likelihood the first living beings were unicellular creatures without a nervous system; vertebrates begin with fish, and the neocortex of mammals is relatively recent. Although we *do not know the causes* (an inherent characteristic of living matter?; the influence of environment?; natural selection?), it is certain that living beings have progressed toward a larger brain and that man appears as the crowning glory, the culmination of that evolution. This is not a matter of a theory or "evolutionary" hypothesis, but a scientific, incontestable conclusion of paleontology.

We represent the result of the complexification of life; man is not independent of the animal scale. Studying the brain of today's animals therefore involves recognizing the stages through which the cerebrum passed in its development toward man. Naturally, we must avoid identifying today's animals with our ancestors. The study of the chimpanzce is very interesting because it is the animal of today whose brain is next in complexity to man's, but paleontology teaches us that it does not belong to the human line of descendants. It is a distant cousin, very specialized, and our common ancestors date back to the Tertiary period, millions of years ago.

At that distant epoch, several lineages must have become differentiated among very primitive little monkeys. Some of them, such as the apes and the anthropoids, adapted themselves to certain environments; one of them, the Hominidae, remained much more primitive and, over the ages, its improvement was limited to its brain. We are beginning to be familiar with a series of stages in that evolution: the Tertiary Oreopithecus, the Australopithecus, and the prehumans (Pithecanthropus-Sinanthropus). The essential part of the process of *"hominization"* * lies, in all likelihood, in mutations producing species with brains more and more rich in neurons. But that requires at the same time a complete organic transformation. For man to come into being, the *biped stance* was necessary, for by changing the way the head was held it permitted the increase in cranial volume that was required for the growth of the brain, while at the same time freeing the hand and developing the face in such a way as to facilitate speech. The interesting thing about the Australopithecines, whose cerebral volume was close to that of the anthropoids, is that they were already completely biped.

There is another important biological aspect of "homini-

Brain of the Australopithecus (right) and the Sinanthropus Pekinensis (left) as shown by cranial models. The dawn of consciousness?

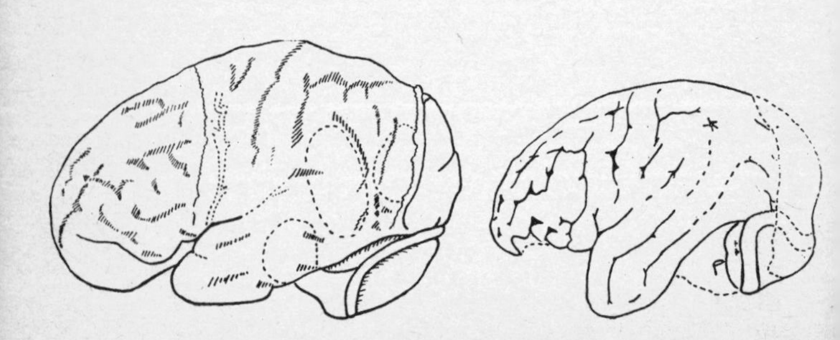

zation". Compared to the ape, man has a *slowed-down rate of growth.* Instead of reaching puberty and adulthood within five to eight years, he must mature slowly. Not only does he have a more highly developed brain, but at birth this brain is incomplete and is constructed slowly during childhood and adolescence. This slowed-down rate of growth in beings for whom the acquired predominates over the innate is of great importance. As has been said, it makes the child somewhat resemble the fetus of a monkey. Progress proceeds by way of a preservation of primitive characteristics, a nonspecialization.

At the beginning, the Hominidae, in spite of their very human characteristics, remained animals with insufficient brains: it was only at a late stage in "hominization" that a mutation led to true man. From skeletons, it is very difficult to pinpoint the stage at which the transition took place. Not that the appearance of true man occurred gradually, for such things always happen by an abrupt mutation, a change of biological nature. It is rather because we cannot affirm with certainty that such-and-such a being was or was not man. Most paleontologists, basing their conclusions both on skeletons and on traces of the activity of the corresponding beings, tend to classify the Australopithecines as apes (the most recent discoveries credit them with the first chipped-stone implements) and the prehumans as men because of their tools, their use of fire, etc.

Actually, it is difficult to say precisely what a prehuman, still an animal, could have done better than a chimpanzee. The only sure criterion lies in religious art and the cult of the dead. Now, these appear only with Neanderthal and Cro-Magnon men, who as it happens possessed a cranial volume equal to today's. They already had our brain, therefore, except that the prefrontal region of Neanderthal man was still insufficient. Whatever their technical feats, can one give the name of men to creatures of the Pithecanthropus-Sinanthropus order whose cranial volume was only 900 to 1,000 cc. – that is, at an intermediate point between today's anthropoid (450 cc.) or the Australopithecus (600 cc.) and true man (1,450 cc.)?

Judging by the coefficient of cephalization, these creatures would fill in the lacuna between today's ape and man: the ape has one-fourth as many neurons; they would have merely one-half. We thus begin to understand how a simple natural mutation climaxing a series of oriented mutations resulted in the human brain at the end of a prehistorical period of 600,000 years from the time of the Pithecanthropus, or of a period of 50,000 years from the time of Cro-Magnon man (who, however, was not the first *homo sapiens*).

But, contrary to what happens in the case of animals, the original mutation endowing man with his nature and with his brain was not enough to make this being stand revealed immediately in his full human dimension. The brain provides merely the *possibility* of being a man, particularly an aptitude for vocalization. It does not provide a language, the means of thinking; for this it is necessary that man learn socially and culturally how to use his brain, a task that will never be finished. There is also the difficulty of distinguishing, at the beginning, between an animal that is exhibiting all its potentialities and a man who has not learned to develop them fully. With man a threshold was crossed, but the existence of stages which lead one to conclude, mistakenly, that there is continuity makes the historical moment of this step very difficult to determine.

History of a brain

The progressive chart of cerebral development which nature presents to us today – and which paleontology certifies to be the reflection of that history of the past in which man explains himself by the evolutionary laws of life – continues to be filled in right before our eyes. It is no longer a question of the improvement of species, but of the way in which each human individual acquires his brain in the course of his development. We are amazed that our species can have had some unicellular being as its distant ancestor one or two billion years ago. But each of us comes from a unicellular being much humbler than an infusorian or an amoeba and yet already ourself, with all our potentialities. Man is not at first a brain capable of thought; he is at first a single cell, an *egg* * whose behavior is almost nonexistent because its parasitism within the maternal uterus is enough to take care of all its needs. In

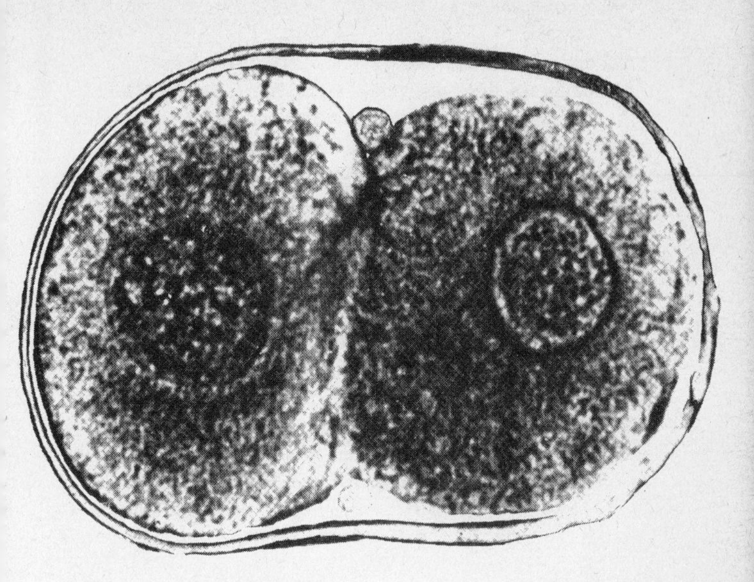

The beginnings of man: the egg has just divided into two parts.

its chemical constitution – that is, by its organization – this egg is already a human being and an individual, though in an imperfect state of being. Its essential property lies in its future, its potentialities. The adult's brain is present potentially in the constitution of the egg, and certain defects or aptitudes of that adult brain will depend on the nature of this egg and all the factors that have an effect upon it at this moment.

It is not possible for us to know how life went about passing from the amoeba to man in the course of thousands of years. On the other hand, *embryology* explains more and more about how the human organism, in the process of its development from egg to adult, builds its brain by a veritable *self-construction* requiring no outside engineer. Here also a remarkable parallelism links the stages of nervous formation to psychophysiological activity. In the course of his development, man is always man; but he nevertheless passes through stages of organization that correspond more or less to the stages at which less evolved animals, today's witnesses to what our ancestors were like, have remained. If the newborn human has such a restricted behavior and almost no psychism, this is because his unfinished brain does not function; at birth, the mesencephalon and the hypothalamus are the only ones among the upper centers that begin to function. Since human superiority lies in having a greater number of neurons, one may suppose that the essence of the successive mutations involved in "hominization" has consisted of a larger number of divisions of the nerve cells in the course of development. It will therefore undoubtedly be possible one day to augment the brain of a chimpanzee fetus or to give a child more neurons by artificial means. What will be the result?

As we have said, human superiority depends not only upon the nature of the brain, but also upon the slowness with which it constructs itself. Unfinished at birth, it is completed in the human social environment, and this environment will be necessary for the brain to be normal. A child *isolated* at birth from the human environment shows not merely educative deficiencies, but cerebral deficiencies as well; he degenerates, because his brain does not develop normally and loses certain potentialities permanently. A sequestered child becomes an idiot; a child reared by wolves *(wolf-children *)* imitates wolves and becomes dehumanized. Not needing to use his aptitude for articulation and not learning a language, he does not develop his language centers at the appropriate time and subsequently becomes very poorly equipped to learn human language. It is likely that his intelligence must suffer from the absence of an inner language and the insufficiency of the corresponding centers. On the other hand, although it is known that a deaf child living in a normal environment becomes mute, he remains much more normal cerebrally because of all the cultural and social influences that reach him. He can therefore subsequently be given an inner language, either by the medium of hand movements or by being taught how to speak by re-education. A deaf child often is behind and lacks skill for abstract language, but he does not show any real intellectual deficiency.

Anatomically, a human brain is not finished – that is, does not possess a complete nervous network – until approximately the age of seven. This age, called the age of reason, accordingly marks the moment when the construction of the brain, with its possibilities of permanent failure, makes way for the acquired art of using this brain, which is a realm in which possibilities are the most durable. However, it would be a mistake to regard the brain of a seven-year-old, though anatomically complete, as a mature brain from a functional point of view, and educative errors can still impede this physiological maturation and deprive the adult of important possibilities. It is only toward the age of eighteen that the electroencephalogram becomes that of an adult.

Four factors play a role in the construction of the brain. The first is *heredity* *; that is, the individual constitution depending on the chemical nature of the original egg, which is a spontaneous aptitude to produce a brain of a given type by virtue of the ineluctable tendency of the organism to construct itself. The properties of the *inner environment* * make up the second factor: differences in composition of the various parts, reciprocal interactions, hormones, etc., which guide the harmonious construction of the brain. Third factor: the individual's *outer environment:* this is first of all the uterine environment, which provides the nutriments needed for growth. The outer environment, particularly after birth, becomes the source of innumerable sensorial data much more complex than those coming from the inner environment; they are extremely important in stimulating the growth of the nervous system. The cultural and social types of information without which the human brain would not develop completely are a special variety of these sensorial data.

But there exists a fourth factor too often neglected. Growth is not simply passive, like that of a plant, the interaction between a living force and its environment. While we can intervene actively by trying to provide the child, and even the fetus, with a suitable environment, the child himself, as his consciousness comes to life, can *intervene on his own* in the completion of his brain and his personality. He must be provided with the taste, the desire for what will be useful to him; it must not imposed upon him, he must be made to search it out for himself. People still tend far too much to regard man's psychic and mental characteristics as a property of the soul, forgetting their dependence on cerebral equilibrium, which requires a well-constructed brain – that is, one that is fully human and that its possessor has learned to use correctly. A child of five to seven, though he must still mature and learn, already possesses a personality and character which will be only slightly modifiable subsequently. It is a mistake to believe that we are dealing here with an *innate* * result of heredity. More important than heredity is the influence of the environment during the early years, for it becomes a part of the very nature of a human being by contributing to the formation of his brain. Depending on his environment, the same individual can be different. Human malleability is great. Certain environments are humanizing and bring out all the fortunate possibilities of heredity; others are dehumanizing. The great differences between adults and even between children of various races and classes are to be explained much more by environment than by heredity, contrary to what racists affirm. This does not mean that heredity does not play a very important role in conditioning differences in aptitude, particularly intellectual, but from this point of view there exist practically no appreciable differences between races.

Even at birth, heredity is not the only factor at work. Many defects that show up at this time are not at all hereditary but result from unfavorable conditions of fetal life. Except in special cases, it is very difficult to distinguish between what comes from heredity, genetic anomalies, and what comes from the various environmental factors, and this is all the more true because multiple causes can combine their effects. Often much more is known about rare and serious anomalies than about more normal individuals, and this greatly limits the possibilities of eugenic selection.

Without going into the details of the formation of the brain, we should point out that two periods are extremely important: the first weeks of intra-uterine life, when the cerebral organ is formed, and the first two years after birth, when this organ rapidly matures and begins to function. Experimental embryology, by acting upon the various factors of development it is clarifying, has brought into existence innumerable monsters that make us understand the laws of normal development. In this way we shall learn the reasons for natural monstrosities and shall be able to avoid them.

The nerve centers appear very early, in the first week of development, when the individual is still nothing but a germ * in which the cells are arranged in various layers. A *neural tube* is formed in the dorsal part of the germinal skin tissue by a fold toward the inside (this is what explains the existence of a cavity in adult nerve centers). It is not by chance that the nerve centers are formed here. A neighboring region releases a chemical substance called an *organizer* * which brings about the formation of the neural tube. By transplanting this organizing region, it has been possible to cause nerve centers to develop in an abnormal position and to endow an embryo with supplementary nerve centers. The organizing substance can also be injected locally.

The encephalon is at first a simple vesicle. In the course of the embryonic period *(embryo *),* the formative period for the organs, from the second to the eighth week, this vesicle gives birth to the various parts of the adult encephalon. It divides in two. The posterior part is at the origin of the lower encephalic centers and divides in turn into three parts. The anterior part, the origin of the brain itself, divides

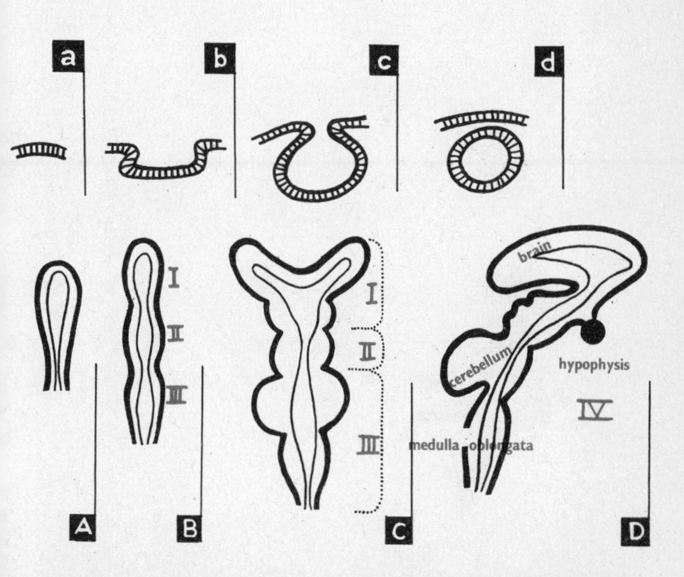

The origin of the nervous system.
Above: formation of the spinal cord, beginning with the skin of the back of the embryo. Below: formation of the various parts of the encephalon.

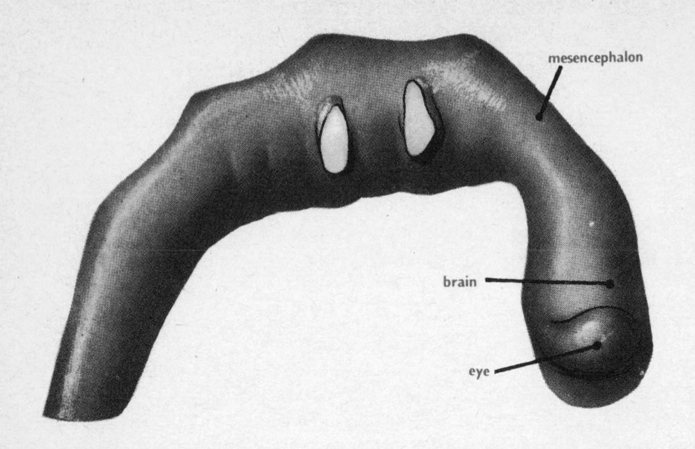

also in two: the cerebral cortex and most of the corpora striata come from the first vesicle, called the *telencephalon,* whereas the thalamus and the hypothalamus come from the second vesicle, or *diencephalon.* The lateral ventricles are the telencephalic cavity, the third ventricle the diencephalic

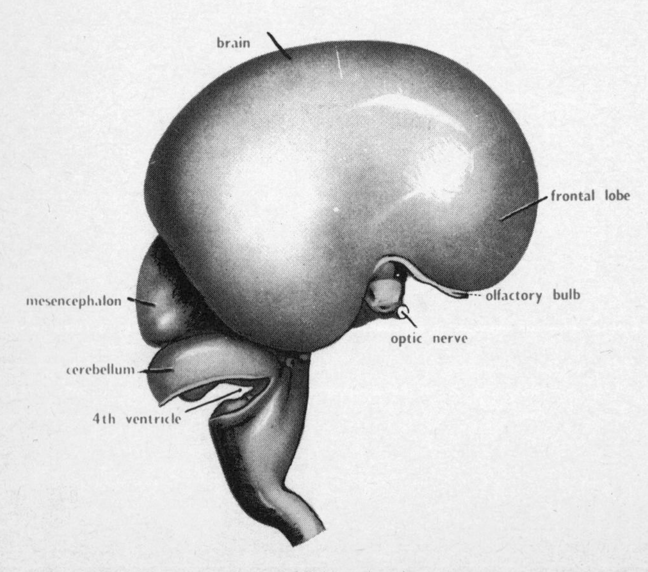

The encephalon of a human embryo at 32 days (above). at 70 days (below).

cavity. In the course of subsequent development, derivatives of the telencephalon and of the diencephalon form a single mass in mammals.

At the beginning of the fetal period *(fetus *)*, at eight weeks, when the human form begins to appear, the young human being, provided with a relatively enormous head, has an anatomically formed brain. But the nerve cells in it are still undifferentiated. It is only subsequently that they will grow their processes. However, very quickly, the definitive substance will be formed. At mid-term, the fetus has at its disposal all of its nerve cells, those which will serve the individual throughout his entire life, because neurons are too complicated to be able to divide and be renewed.

The relatively long fetal period witnesses the completion of the construction of all the organs and their entry into

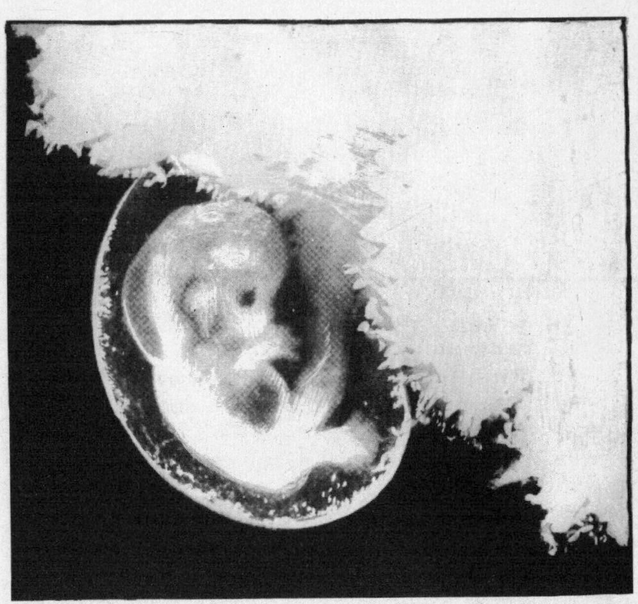

Eight-week-old embryo.

action. Above all, it witnesses the initiation of all the harmonizing mechanisms that make the organism a unity – not a collection of cells, but an individual. This integration depends more than anything else on the maturing of the nervous system. Like an amoeba or a white blood corpuscle, the nerve fibers emitted by the nerve cells make their way in the centers or the tissues and establish all the contacts needed for functioning. These connections, which bridge much smaller distances in the fetus than in the adult, depend partly on the nervous system's natural tendency to grow, partly on the dynamic influence of general factors such as certain hormones, and partly on the specific attraction exercised by certain tissues on the nervous system. Grafting an additional limb brings about the creation of nerves destined to innervate it; the muscle attracts its motor nerve and, according to whether its anatomical position makes it flexor or extensor, the connections in the spinal cord will be harmoniously constructed. One sees in this way the gradual development of all reflex behavior; that is, the possibility of acts that are as yet useless but that will be necessary subsequently.

Life on the outside – even breathing, which normally does not begin until the ninth month – is thus possible in the seventh month. The eye is anatomically complete well before birth. A first elementary reflex response – a motor reaction to the skin's being excited – has been noted at as early as eight and a half weeks. It may be found surprising that certain functions can take place without practice. This is because exercise does not seem to be necessary for that which matures automatically. Normally in tadpoles locomotion develops little by little. But if the animal is anesthetized, it cannot exercise, and yet nervous maturation comes about all the same. Upon waking, it will not be functionally behind the normal animal that had seemed to be training itself.

The lower centers are the ones that develop first. The brain lags far behind; its maturation takes place after birth, by the same processes. If, for example, the newborn infant does not walk even though his medullary motor structures are fully developed, this is because of the immaturity of the psychomotor cells, called the pyramidal cells. Walking does not depend on exercise but on the growth of those

Growth of a nerve fiber between 10 : 30 and 12 : 30.

fibers which, from their starting point in the brain, reach the spinal cord. Their maturity is judged by their myelination; they are completed only when covered by their white sheath of myelin. * A large part of the nervous functions depend in this way upon maturation alone, so that it is not possible to hasten the acquisition of functions.

However, the usefulness of a function and its exercise are not without importance in good nervous maturation. It has been observed that, if the eyelids of a young monkey are sewed up at birth, its visual cerebral neurons will not mature. After a certain time, it will be permanently blind. It is cerebral maturation that makes a baby babble in its cradle, but if the sounds do not become socially interesting as communication, as in the case of the wolf-child, the development of the language centers will be impeded. Once the normal age for their development is passed, language apprenticeship will become difficult. On the other hand, a deaf child preserves a much greater aptitude for ceasing to be mute.

The fundamental law of cerebral development – namely, the possibility of possessing later on a completely normal brain, enjoying all the human aptitudes (this is exceptional still today) – requires that cerebral maturation always find not only the physical but also the cultural and affective environment that favors it. Nothing can be done when it is too early, but in a very short time it is too late. Only the adult, when his brain is well formed and he has learned how to get from it everything of which it is capable, will have at his disposal a completed organ. He will preserve it in good shape only by making it always function correctly – that is, by continuing to progress right into advanced old age, for aging, if normal, should not upset cerebral functioning.

The network of thought

The activity of the brain, like that of any other organ, depends on the material functioning of the living cells that make it up. If this activity seems to be of a very special type, that is because the cellular organization of the nervous system is of a special nature. In the other organs, each cell is like a micro-organ and the functioning of the whole is the sum of all the elementary functionings. When it comes to the nervous system, and particularly the brain, which is distinguished only by its greater complexity, the isolated nerve cell is in no way a small brain. Specializing in the reception, emission, and conduction of messages, it is only one element of an immense interconnected circuit. A cerebral neuron does not think, or does not produce thought, any more than a triode in a calculating machine performs operations by itself. What makes possible the nerve-reflex command in the spinal cord or thought in the brain is *the associated and harmonious functioning of all the neurons.*

Nerve cells, which are closely related to skin cells, were originally ordinary cells. Although they are all alike in putting out multiple processes that provide the network of interconnections, they nonetheless are divided into very different types. Let us point out first of all that the nerve centers are not made up exclusively of neurons. There exists a supporting tissue, the *neuroglia,* whose functions are not yet well understood. High-speed motion-picture photography has shown that their mobile processes seem to massage the neurons. The neuroglia is connected with the origin of cerebral tumors.

The cerebral neurons have multiple processes *(multipolar neurons).* In addition to their *axon,* * a transmitting process which is in general fairly long and which can remain in the gray matter or which can form the white matter after enclosing itself in a sheath of myelin, the cerebral neurons have a number of receiving processes, the *dendrites.* * In general, the dendrites are more ramified and have no myelin, like the cell body – the central region of the cell which has the nucleus and is called the *somatoplasm.* * Differences arise from the size of the cell body, whose diameter varies from 5 to 100 thousandths of a millimeter, from the number and arrangement of the dendrites, and from the diameter and length of the axon. This axon may be short and stay in the gray matter next to the cell body; or it may by longer, passing into the white matter and terminating in the gray matter of another lobe on the same side, or on the other side, or in the central gray nuclei. The maximum length, of about a yard, is attained by certain psychomotor pyramidal cells; their axon, descending into the encephalon, terminates in the spinal cord, where it is in contact with the medullary motor neurons. If the cell body is frontal, for example, the axon terminates in the lumbar region.

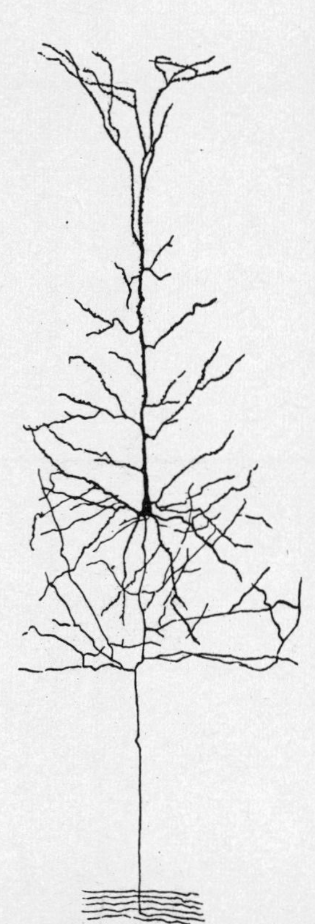

Pyramidal neuron of the brain.

The 14 billion neurons of the cortex, together with their pro-

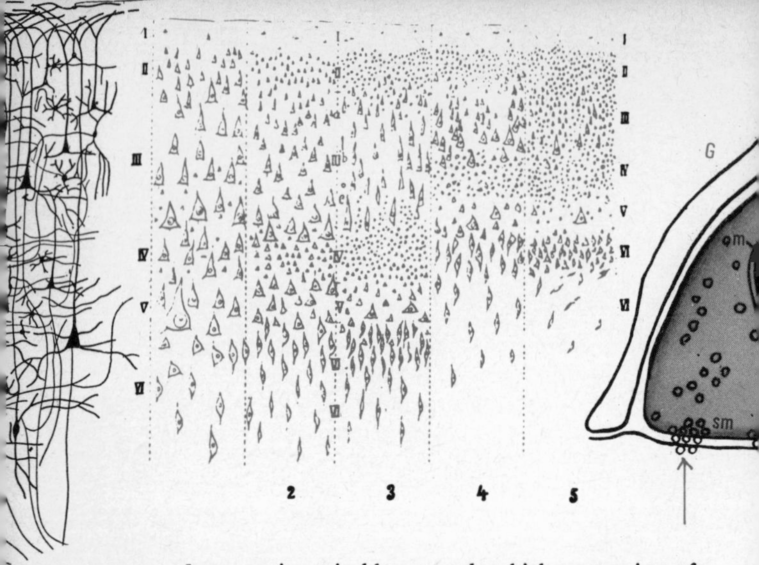

cesses, form an inextricable network which anatomists of former days compared to a kind of padding; they could make out in it only fibers and cells, without distinguishing their limits. The conception of the neuron, of distinct nerve cells with a body and multiple processes, did not come into existence before the end of the nineteenth century, thanks to the discovery of methods that made it possible to proceed to a kind of chemical isolation by giving a special coloring to some nerve cells with all their processes. The most valuable is the Golgi and Ramon y Cajal silver method, which laid the foundations for the histology of the nerve centers.

This inextricable network is made up of independent cells manifoldly interconnected. There is never actual continuity between two cells but contact through close *contiguity* at the points of interconnection, called *synapses,* * where recent studies with the electronic microscope have clearly shown a double separating membrane. Very many types of more or less extended synapses exist, some between fibers and some between fibers and cell body. This independence of the elementş of the network explains the reactions of *Wallerian degeneration* *: when a fiber is cut, the part which

Various types of neurons of the cerebral cortex, from the surface (above) to the white matter (below). The granule cells and the pyramidal cells can be recognized. Structure of the cerebral zones. Cyto-architecture. From top to bottom, the six layers: I granular; 2, 3, 4 homotypical; 5 granular.

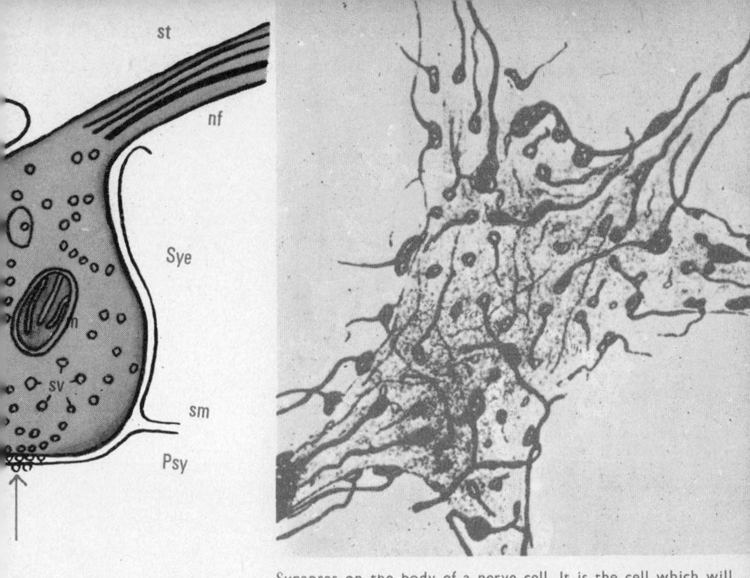

Synapses on the body of a nerve cell. It is the cell which will produce the synthesis of the messages received by the various synapses

is separated from the cell body – that is, from the nucleus – dies and degenerates. Whereas in the peripheral nerves the central end connected to the nucleus can regenerate the destroyed part, this is not true in the case of the centers. Lesions in them are irreparable; there is no regeneration, no multiplication of neurons to replace the destroyed cell bodies.

However complex it may be, the structure of the cerebral cortex is known today in detail, and the neuronic structure of all regions *(cyto-architecture *)* and their interconnections may be found in immense atlases. Two categories of neurons are especially important. The effector element sends out orders – above all motor orders – from the brain toward the basal ganglia or lower centers. These are the *pyramidal neurons,* * including the large psychomotor pyramidal cells located in front of the fissure of Rolando, which control directly, as guided by the will, all the peripheral motor neurons of the opposite side. The receptor element is the cerebral sensorial neuron (esthesioneure) which, by means of numerous synapses, receives impulses

Diagram of a synapse seen through an electronic microscope: sm - synaptic membrane. Sye - bouton. Psy - postsynaptic element. sv - synaptic vesicles, no doubt containing the chemical mediator. m - mitochondrias. nf - nerve fiber.

coming from the sense organs and from sensory fibers along the ascending sensorial tracts. The pyramidal cell owes its name to its triangular cell body bearing at its summit a principal dendrite which rises, with ramifications, toward the surface of the cortex, whereas the axon begins at the base. The receptor cell is a much smaller multipolar neuron, called a granule cell, which appears in clusters.

These neurons make up the entrances and exits of the brain. Whereas some of them are disseminated throughout the cortex, there exist in the neocortex neurons of execution and reception that are localized in certain zones and that have precise functions imposed upon them by their connections. Such is the basis of what have been called *cerebral localizations.* One does not localize thought; one localizes the psychomotor neurons of a certain region of the body, or the receptor neurons of a certain sensitivity. Whereas, for example, in the primitive brain of the rhinencephalon, neurons of execution and reception have a diffuse distribution, in certain zones of the neocortex neurons have a *somatotopical* * localization – that is, one can precisely locate in the cortex the zones that correspond to the various muscles and sensory receptors. In front of the fissure of Rolando one finds, from top to bottom, the psychomotor neurons of the lower limbs, the trunk, the upper limbs, the head, and the neck. Behind this fissure, at the same level, are the neurons that act as receivers for the cutaneous and muscular sensitivity of these various regions. The occipital lobe includes the visual cerebral receptors, distributed in the shape of a true cortical retina: a peripheral retina along the lips of the *calcarine* fissure on the inner surface and a central retina (fovea *) at the end of the lobe. The temporal lobe contains the cortical receptors of hearing, the cortical cochlea.

Whereas, like the motor paths, the paths of cutaneous sensitivity are crossed, one hemisphere being connected to the opposite side of the body, the optic and auditory paths are not completely crossed and there exist receptors connected to both hemispheres. This is the case of the central retina. The taste receptors are localized at the level of the tongue's cutaneous sensitivity, those of smell in front of the rhinencephalon where the olfactory system begins. These zones are very important for the execution of orders or

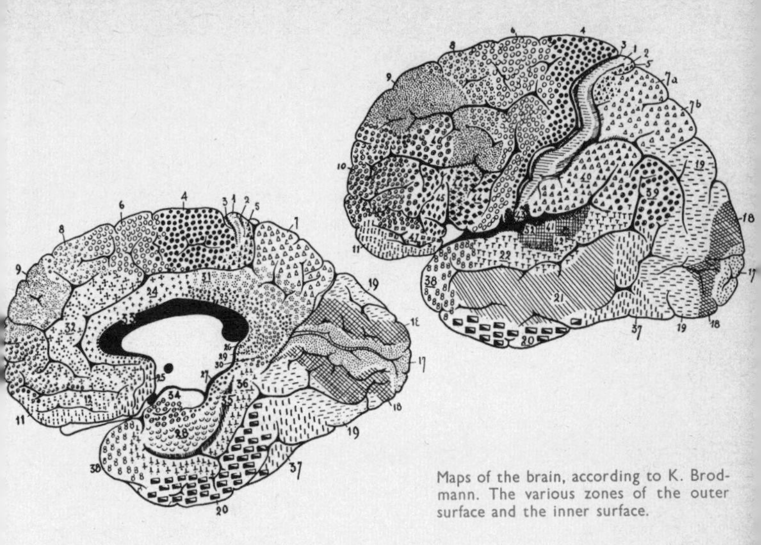

Maps of the brain, according to K. Brodmann. The various zones of the outer surface and the inner surface.

sensory reception (sensations), and their lesion causes irreparable damage. But, as we shall see, they are merely an element of precision in command and reception, both of which also have less localized mechanisms with a somewhat different function.

All cerebral functioning uses multiple, complex neuronic circuits combining sensorial receptors and effector neurons. In these, localizations are much less strict and the possibilities of substitution and of sidetracked circuits in the case of lesions are much more considerable. Surprise is often expressed at the fact that, except for the previously mentioned zones, even extensive cerebral lesions often have only slight effects. The reason is that in such an interconnected network, it is difficult to cut off all connections between starting point and terminal point, and this is all the more true because these connections are not made only on the surface of the cortex; connections between the various parts of the surface are also provided indirectly by relays in the basal centers. What seems to be separated by a surface lesion remains connected underneath. Modern experimentation has even shown that these deep connections are the more important ones.

What counts, as we have seen, is not the absolute number

of neurons, but the density of the interconnected network. Suppressing one part of the network has no effect on the density of what is left. Pasteur, his brain mutilated by hemiplegia, retained his intelligence, because though he had fewer neurons, he had nonetheless preserved his cerebral structures as far as the essential regions were concerned. The cerebral network functions as a unit within which it is possible to localize only certain circuits in certain zones. The only ones that are strictly localized and capable of being destroyed easily are the mechanisms of execution and precision reception at the command of consciousness and will. By studying the neurological aspect of these functions, we shall gain a detailed knowledge of their cerebral mechanisms, whether localized or not. Our knowledge is not yet sufficiently developed for us to know the exact role of the various neurons in over-all functioning as well as we know their structures. We are merely beginning to unravel the complex neuronic circuits of language, memory, etc., and their place inside the cortex. Although we can roughly mark off certain centers on the surface of the brain, we know that we are not indicating the peculiar functions of the neurons of that region, but rather the seat of complex circuits involving hundreds of neurons that we do not yet know how to analyze. It is therefore not necessary for the moment to know the details of the architecture of the cerebral neuronic network in which a given neuron may, depending on the circumstances, fill extremely diverse roles because its interconnections, though anatomically fixed, are, as we shall see, physiologically variable. Let us be satisfied with indicating the general outlines.

The largest part of the cerebral cortex, the neocortex, has six very regular cellular layers, going from the surface inward: between the inner and outer association-layers are two layers called *granular* layers, the predominant neurons of which are granule cells, and two *pyramidal* layers, the predominant neurons of which are pyramidal. A granular layer alternates with a pyramidal one. This cortex, which is called *homotypical*, in which all the layers are present, gives way in the zones of sensorial reception to a purely granular cortex without pyramidal layers, whereas the motor zones are *agranular*, having only pyramidal layers. In the primitive cortex of the rhinencephalon, the layers are less numerous and less distinct.

Classical anatomy pictured nerve paths as rectilinear, made up of chains of neurons. The structure of the cerebral cortex is quite different; it is a neuronic network with multiple paths and links in which numerous ramifications converge and diverge. Of particular importance are the closed chains in which activation can continue in one place by turning in a circle, and the retroactive circuits which leave one neuron and rejoin it by more or less direct paths. Everything is interconnected, but in a harmonized architecture that facilitates or hinders connections.

Cerebral functioning

The histologist who analyzes the thinking network cannot draw any conclusions from it about the mechanisms of thought. Gone, happily, are the days when men hoped to find in the brain, in some material form, psychic processes, the seat of consciousness, or storehouses of images. Seeing the cogwheels of a machine at rest does not tell us how it works. The mind depends on the brain, but the brain must function, be active. The mind is not a material product that can be localized and, so to speak, isolated; it is a *functional* product, conditioned by the harmonious activity of the thinking network. Are we going to ask the physiologist to "collect" and to record the mind? That would be a serious mistake. The physiologist has no way of encountering what is mental or spiritual *in itself;* he knows only the physical or chemical material phenomena that occur in the brain. It is these phenomena which are the condition of what is spiritual, its organic aspect. An understanding of phenomena which is necessary and enlightening in its own way cannot be expected to replace a specific psychological understanding of these phenomena.

What takes place in the brain during thinking? Let us observe first of all that the cerebral activation required for thought comes from the outside, beginning with the senses. This confirms the opinion of realist philosophy according to which everything in the intelligence comes from the senses. Messages from the senses contributed, as we have seen, to the construction of the brain; they are even more necessary to cerebral activity. Working on cats, Bremer isolated the brain from most sensorial messages by a mesencephalic section. This *deafferentation* deactivated the brain and plunged it into the unconsciousness of sleep. It is well known that sensorial repose helps bring sleep.

Like the functioning of any nerve center, cerebral functioning is reflex in origin, the switching of certain sensorial messages to certain motor neurons. A needle pricks me, and I pull it away. But, whereas in the case of a lower center such as the spinal cord, in which the nervous network is fairly simple, messages will be merely passed along to the center with limited central activity, in the case of the brain the higher senses and general sensitivity constantly bring multiple activating messages through the points of entry of the network, whose complex organization is activated as a whole *permanently*. The messages can circulate within the brain along innumerable neuronic circuits without necessarily being switched to motor neurons. This switching will take place only in certain cases, and particularly only if one wills it to. On the other hand, the activated brain no longer needs a constant supply of sensorial messages; it continues to function *autonomously*. The sensorial rest that may lead to sleep also makes it possible to shut oneself up in one's thoughts, to obtain a purely cerebral functioning from the brain. At will also, without receiving any messages, we can activate our motor neurons and give a response that will not be reflex. The complex activation of the brain therefore makes it possible for the brain to be no longer bound to the automatism of reflex switching and to be capable of autonomy, and therefore of spontaneity. Once activated, it is the master of its activity; in particular, it can *reproduce* a past activity thanks to *memory* and imagination; it can be *creative* – that is, it can organize various types of activity. The difference between this and reflex automatism depends exclusively on cerebral complexity: a beginning of autonomy and independent activity can be seen even in the spinal cord.

What are thought, consciousness, mind, from the biological point of view? As a matter of fact, this autonomous cerebral activity called *interiority* in the spiritual sense of the word is provided by the inner activity of the brain where cerebral equivalence – the reflection of the outside world and of ourselves – takes place. It is because the interior of animals' brains is inadequate that they are not capable of man's interiorized and reflective spirituality.

What does this nervous interiority consist of? In a man-made machine, consisting of inert and inanimate cogwheels, some kind of *external* energy must be provided in order to pass from inactivity to activity. For example, the current that heats the filaments of triodes is turned on; the "wheels" will be the passive apparatus that transmits signals. However great the likeness between the nervous network and an electric network may be, they differ essentially in that the nervous network is made up of *living* cells – that is, of elements in which life does not allow total inactivity. Repose is only a lesser activity during which the cell that is doing nothing when judged from an external, functional point of view is nevertheless engaging in intense chemical activity simply to stay alive: the filament is always red, and the apparently inactive cell needs energy; it is expending, and needs oxygen and such aliments as glucose. In the case of the cell, working does not mean entering into activity, but entering into superactivity, and therefore having increased needs. Moreover, this activity is literally an activity, very different from passive conduction in an inert circuit. The neuron, like all living cells, is excitable – that is, it *reacts* to certain external modifications to which it is *sensitive*. It will not be a passive conductor, but will give its own response as determined by its sensitivity. Being active therefore implies an essential transformation of the living "cogwheel," which exhibits not simply a hyperfunctioning, but an increased and accelerated sensitivity and *excitability** – what is called a state of *excitation*. *

Thus, the neuron never knows total inactivity, the true repose that for it would correspond to inertness and therefore death. This does not mean that it merely oscillates between a state of superactivity and one of apparent repose. For one thing, superactivity can be caused either by the element's being excited by external excitants or by the self-excitation of the element, which may enter spontaneously into activity under, for example, a chemical influence. For another, repose also corresponds to two quite different states: simple inactivity of the element which, not being excited, is satisfied with just living, and the state of super-rest, in which excitability is diminished and slowed down. In the latter case, the neuron is no longer in repose, but in a state of active *braking* to which the term *inhibition* * is applied. What we have here is not a passive state but a characteristic modality of cellular activity requiring an expenditure of energy and succeeding eventually in putting the element out of circuit; external excitations no longer reach it, for it wards them off. The neuron thus oscillates unceasingly from one side to the other of the average state, repose, the basic activity of life – fluctuating between excitation (tiring work activity directed toward the exterior, the reception and emission of messages) and inhibition (activity involving braking, withdrawal, being cut off from the exterior, and therefore more complete repose).

Cerebral functioning as a whole, which is the basis of psychism, is to be explained by a *fluctuating and harmonious distribution in time and space* of neuronic excitations and inhibitions. The anatomical structures of the thinking network explain nothing. The neurological aspect of thought consists of the variable *structurations* * set up in the network by the alternation between states of excitation and inhibition. These phenomena involve not just isolated neurons; rather, neuronic ensembles – either points of the network or ensembles that have interconnections throughout the cortex – are submitted to *waves* of excitation and inhibition. It would thus be possible to draw up a color chart at any given moment showing all the neurons, with different shades graduated for all the levels between extreme excitation and extreme inhibition. Everything of the same color would be in the same state, making up an ensemble functioning together at the same rhythm. We can therefore have several circuits in the brain functioning simultaneously but independently, thanks to this physiological barrier of the level of excitation. An inhibited zone is completely inactive; a region that is only relatively inhibited can be the seat of slowed-down local activity; and this activity will remain distinct from that of more excited zones. A message will be received or emitted by the brain only if the inhibition barrier does not stand in the way.

This reflection of the world and of ourselves that is our brain, with its own life inside us, is therefore made up of an alternation between states of excitation and inhibition:

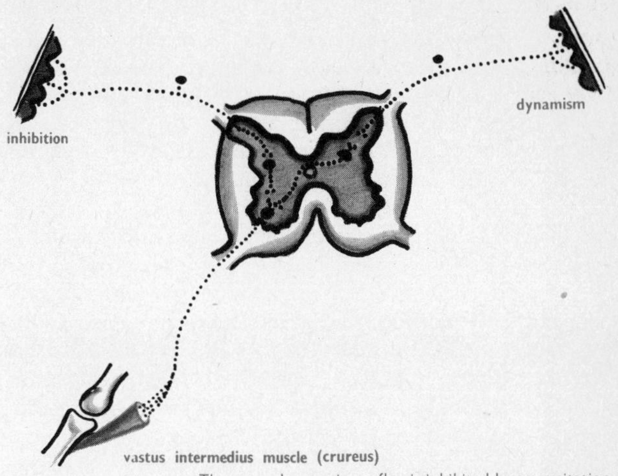

The crossed extension reflex is inhibited by an excitation coming from the same side (Sherrington).

physiological structurations, *mosaics* of functional states, dynamic *patterns* * which, relying on a material activity, have no existence apart from that activity. The Russian school calls them *dynamic stereotypes,* and the Anglo-Saxon school *patterns.* The brain in repose does not contain inactive thought; it is merely an aptitude for being activated, and therefore for thinking. The active brain does not produce thoughts that one might hope to collect independently of it; it is not a mechanism at the command of a thought exterior to it. It gives us the material, organic, and *cerebral* aspect of thought, its *infrastructure,* and leaves to psychology the task of studying thought in itself, its *superstructure,* its spiritual aspect, either by introspection or by the study of behavior. Neurophysiology tells us how the human being thinks with his brain, the organic conditions of his spirituality, but it is not its business to know all the aspects of his spirituality. It is materialist only in appearance, because it concerns itself with the material aspect of existence, but there is no reason for it to encroach upon the domain of philosophy.

How can we understand this veritable motion picture in black, gray, and white that is projected in our brain by these constant fluctuations in time and space of the phenomena of excitation and inhibition within the thinking network activated by messages from the senses?

Early methods of cerebral exploration that flourished between 1870 and 1900 as a result of observations by Broca (language centers) and Fritsch and Hitzig (psychomotor centers) consisted of comparing the effects of cerebral lesions (human pathology and animal experimentation) to corresponding clinical signs, or of observing the effects upon animals of electrical *excitations* localized by means of *electrodes.* * These were capable of giving us information about the localization of certain motor and sensorial centers or the major functions of certain parts of the brain, but they were too crude to give us precise knowledge of intimate functioning. The effect on man of ill-defined lesions that came to light only after death was observed. In the case of animals, experimental neurophysiology was not very psychological: small muscular contractions or convulsive crises were caused by exciting the brain during serious operations on a subject stupefied by anesthetics. What really went on in the brain was not known.

The Russian neurophysiologist Pavlov was the initiator of the analytical study of the active brain. Having observed in his researches the influence of psychic factors on gastric secretion, he wanted to know the cerebral phenomena that gave birth to them. He then had the idea of turning to the phenomenon of *training* and making of it a method of external study of the brain's inner working under the strict conditions of laboratory experimentation on animals (chiefly dogs) and men. What is training if not the acquisition of a new reaction? We respond innately, as a function of nerve connections, to certain messages from the senses by appropriate reactions. An automatic reflex makes anyone who eats an appetizing dish salivate. On the other hand, there are some meaningless signals that arouse no reaction. If a bell rings when we aren't expecting anything, we remain indifferent. But associating the indifferent signal with a significant one – the bell with food – several times, is enough to cause this cerebral *coexistence* of the signals to transfer to the indifferent signal the ability to set off the reaction – in this case, salivation. A new path is created in the brain; upon the innate reflex has been constructed a trained or acquired reflex, which Pavlov called a *conditioned reflex.* *

For such a phenomenon to be possible, one must have at one's disposal a complex center such as the cerebral cortex, rich in unemployed possibilities, in which everything is not a fixed part of the construction as in the spinal cord, but in which any signal can be switched toward any zone of execution. The cerebral conditioned reflex is the basis of memory: when we have learned to react in a certain way, the new path becomes one of the brain's possibilities and it opens up automatically at the appropriate signal or under the effect of the imagination.

By observing the reactions to a given signal of a completely normal animal or man, in a state of calm in order to avoid distractions, or better still by measuring these reactions (counting drops of saliva, for example), it is possible to follow the establishment of the reflex or to analyze its phases when it is established, and to observe everything that modifies it, particularly the influence of other signals acting on the same part or on other parts of the brain. The brain's sensitivity – that is, the neurons' aptness to react, their increased excitability during excitation and decreased excitability during inhibition – is tested from the outside, by the natural path of the senses. This excitation and this inhibition are thus evaluated from the outside by the intensity of the reaction; we can accordingly form an indirect but, as modern methods of direct exploration have confirmed, accurate idea of what is going on in the brain. This is an example of precise experimental neurophysiological research in which the analysis is not based upon an anonymous mechanism, but upon a particular animal with its own temperament and nervous type. (Among other possible applications is the creation of a complete science of animal psychiatry.) This method made it possible for Pavlov to form a good idea of cerebral functioning, well in advance of other physiologists.

Instead of testing cerebral excitability indirectly by means of a signal directed at the senses, one can study the excitability of cerebral neurons by artificial excitants; the easiest to use is the electric excitant. Around 1909, when Pavlov

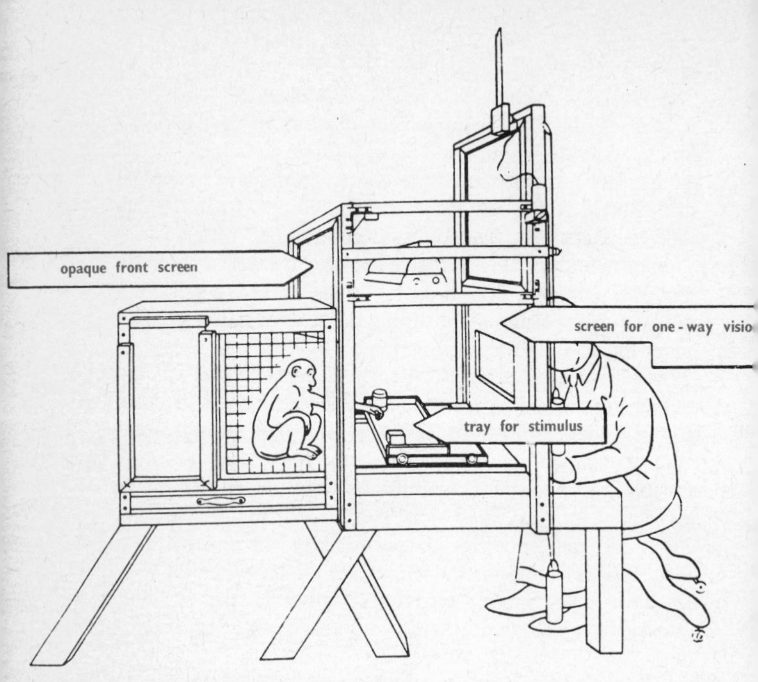

A monkey at work. Formation of conditioned reflexes.
If it succeeds, it will be rewarded.

was exploring the brain from the outside, L. and M. Lapicque showed that there is a connection between electrical excitability and the cellular state. A brief current is needed to excite a rapid-reaction cell, a prolonged one to excite a slow-reaction cell. The measure of the time of electrical excitation, usually a time corresponding to twice the intensity of the minimum, called *rheobasis* * *(chronaxy* *),* makes it possible to assign a figure to the cellular state and its variations. Subsequently, in the period 1923–1928, the Lapicques, for animals, and Bourguignon, for men, showed that the chronaxies of the nerves are modified *(metachronosis* *) by the central processes of excitation and inhibition (phenomenon of *subordination).* A nerve that is easily accessible and excitable from the outside without opening the skin or subjecting the subject to discomfort becomes a test of the central state, like drops of saliva. At the same time, A. and B. Chauchard measured the chronaxies of the cerebral neurons, judging their variations directly either on an opened brain or on a dog prepared ahead of time – that is, with brain-pan removed and the skin sutured above the brain – making it possible to excite the brain of a normal, wide-awake animal as one excites a nerve (this can be done on a rat without removing the bone). Working directly on the brain and on the nerve showed the necessity of operating, like Pavlov, on a normal, wide-awake animal in order to obtain normal figures and instances of inhibition. Under such conditions, variations in the central or peripheral chronaxies provide a good picture of the fluctuations of excitation and inhibition. The

Cat with electrodes in its brain (experiment by Buser and Chatelier).

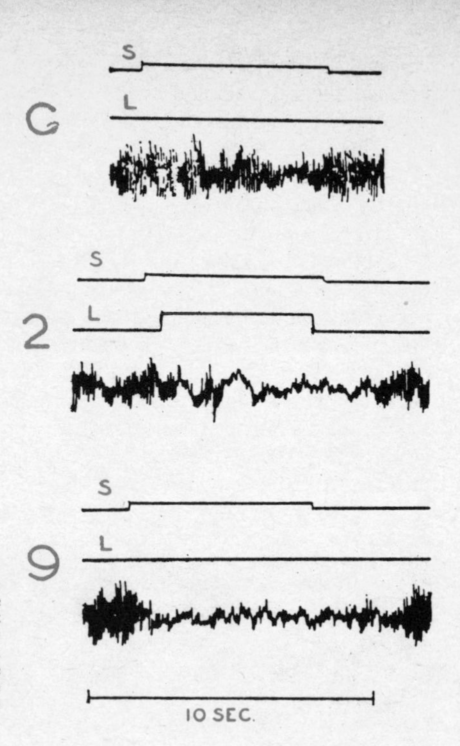

Electric activity of the brain during training. Above: the sound has no effect. Below: at the ninth association, the sound has become effective without the light. In the middle: the effect of the light when the sound is still ineffective, at the 2nd association.

association of chronaximetry and the Pavlovian method is fruitful.

The electrical activity of the brain

Instead of testing the neuron's aptitude for giving a response, it is more direct to judge the neuronic state of excitation or inhibition itself. For that it would be sufficient to register and measure just any manifestation of this state: chemical modification of breathing or metabolism, tiny release of heat that results, release of specific chemical substances, variations of the mineral equilibrium between the neuron and the exterior, *diastases,* * etc. Numerous researches have shown that all these factors vary with the neuronic state, but as things now stand it has not yet been

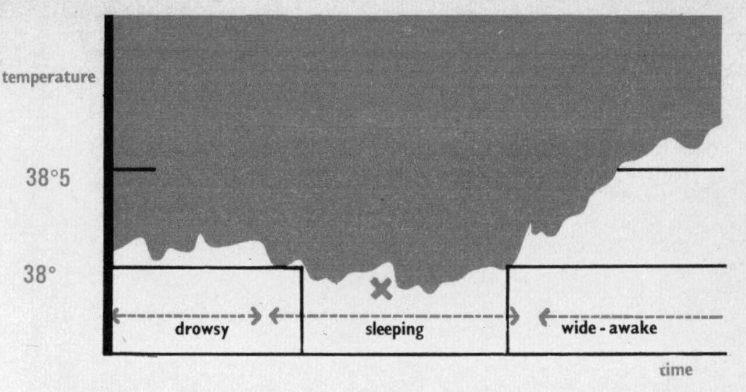

The heat of the brain. Variations in the temperature of the brain of a drowsy, sleeping, and wide-awake cat.

possible to use these observations as a basis for determining precise and simple methods of studying the thinking brain.

Quite different is the case of *electrical* manifestations of nervous activity. These manifestations are not peculiar to the brain, but occur in all living cells. The chemical dynamism of life creates a difference of concentration between the interior of the cell and the exterior, and this

Two laws of electric excitability as a function of time. Slow neuron in B, fast neuron in A. I - rheobasis. t - chronaxy. T - time needed.

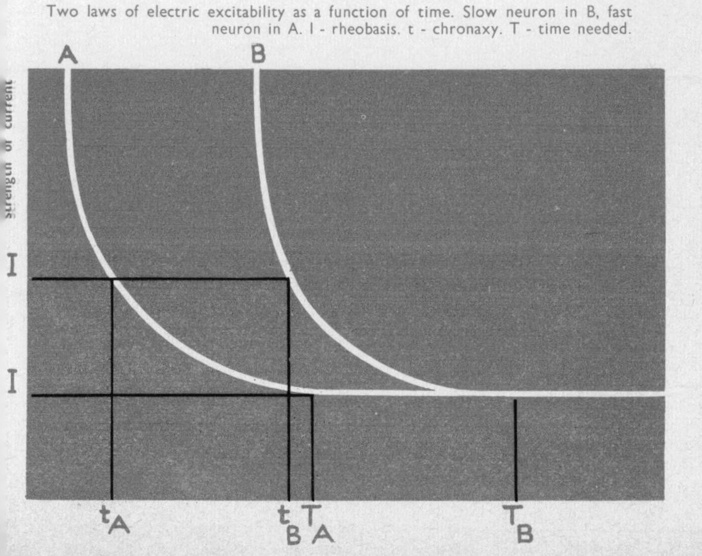

difference is expressed by the existence at the cell's surface of a protective *positive* electrical charge *(polarization *)* which disappears at death. Any excitation of the cell and all the factors to which it is sensitive and which bring into play its excitability and make it react have the effect of diminishing, cancelling, or reversing the surface charge; the cell then increases its chemism to re-establish its normal state. The state of excitation is a cellular depolarization in which the cell is more excitable; the state of inhibition is a superpolarization in which it is less excitable. It can thus be seen that the electrical excitant is the specific excitant. The chronaxy gives the speed of repolarization of the excited cell.

We have known about neuromuscular electricity, in repose and in activity, for a long time, ever since the initial observations of Galvani in 1788 and the detailed studies of Matteucci and Du Bois Reymond more than a century ago. The sensory, motor, or central nervous message (that is, the wave of nervous impulse which the ancients called animal spirits and likened to some subtle fluid circulating in presumably hollow nerves) has been shown to be an electric wave. As a matter of fact, the depolarization of excitation on a nerve does not remain localized; it moves along the nerve to its very end where, by virtue of its power to excite, it activates the innervated element. All nervous functioning depends on the creation, conduction, and switching of successions of electrical nervous *pulsations.** But we must not, on the basis of this, liken the nervous system to a network of inert conductors, mere passive carriers for the phenomenon. Conduction of the impulse is a *self-excitation* – that is to say, every point reacts as living matter to the depolarizing effect that comes along. The electrical wave is in reality only the sign of a complete disturbance of living matter which is translated also into chemical modifications. The characteristics of the impulse, and therefore its ability to excite, will depend on the level of cellular polarization.

Progress in the technique of electrical measurements has made it easier to record nervous impulses, thanks especially to electronic amplifiers and the use of the cathode ray oscillograph, applied to neurophysiology by Erlanger and Gasser in 1923.

The cerebral nervous network, like the nerves, is the seat of unceasing electrical activity that appears in two aspects: modifications of neuronic polarization on the one hand and fluctuations of the emission and conduction of propagated waves of nervous impulse on the other. An excited neuron is depolarized and conducts rapid and numerous impulses; an inhibited neuron is superpolarized, and the impulses, which are scarce and slow, tend to disappear.

How has the study of cerebral electricity become a practical means of knowing the inner workings of cerebral functioning?

Apart from certain previous experiments that had merely shown the reality of the phenomenon, we can say that the modern era of electrical exploration of the brain began in 1929 when the German psychiatrist H. Berger showed that the electrical activity of the human brain could be recorded by placing electrodes on the scalp. From a subject

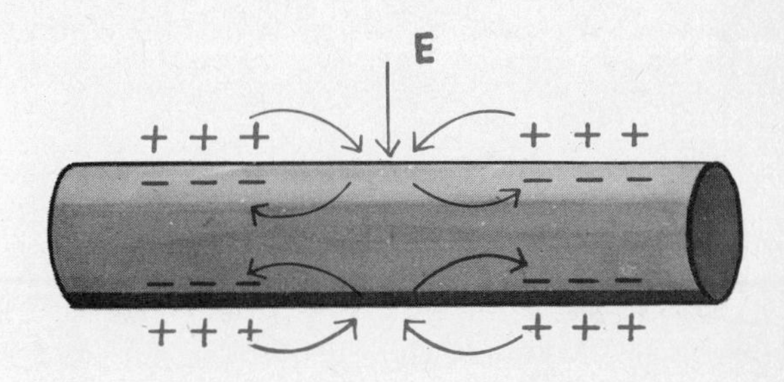

How the nervous impulse is born and is carried.
E - place of excitation.

who was wide-awake but in sensorial repose and calm, he obtained a series of regular pulsations with an average rhythm of 10 per second and an amplitude of 5 to 50 millionths of a volt; he called them *alpha waves.* All cerebral activation (sensorial excitation, mental work, paying attention) causes a blocking * of these waves * and is followed by a more rapid, irregular, and much less intense activity. This is interpreted today as the sign of a desynchronization. In repose, all neurons tend to pulsate synchronously; cerebral work, which is a localized activation, destroys this over-all synchronization.

The reaction of neurophysiologists to Berger's observations, which laid the foundations of electroencephalography, was skeptical. They did not believe that the electrical activity of the brain could be observed at a distance without direct contact between electrodes and neurons, which was the usual method of studying nervous electricity. However, Adrian and Bremer confirmed Berger's results and electroencephalography developed rapidly. For the last eighteen years it has been an independent science with its own specialists and meetings. Considerable progress has been made, thanks particularly to Grey Walter, Gastaut, and Rémond. The activity at numerous points on the scalp

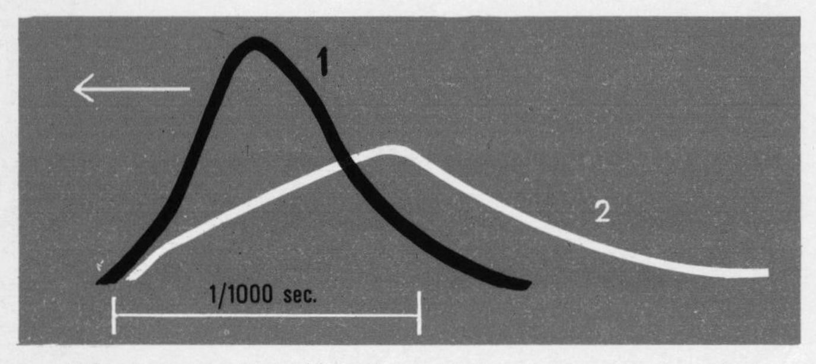

Two nervous impulsions. (1) rapid nerve; intense, brief, and rapid impulsion. (2) slow nerve; weak, long, and slow impulsion.

corresponding to the various cerebral zones (more than 20) is recorded simultaneously. Automatic *analyzers* make it possible to distinguish waves of various frequencies; it is even possible today to obtain directly a map of the electrical state of the brain, objectifying the mosaic of excitation and inhibition.

Spontaneous activity varies with the individual type,

age, and state of the brain. Descriptions have been written of the electrical activity of sleep with its *delta waves,* and the special activity of certain states of anger *(theta waves).* Modifications can be caused by making the brain work, by submitting it to rhythmic excitations *(luminous flicker),* or by modifying its chemism *(hyperpnea *).* In pathology, electrical activity shows characteristic modifications in cerebral tumors that make it possible to localize them (slow waves of cerebral suffering from compression); and an epileptic fit is a real cerebral electrical storm. It is even possible to detect potential epilepsy by electrical signs observed before attacks.

Electroencephalography is a convenient method which is developing constantly. It gives valuable indications about the state of the thinking brain; in particular, the study of electrical manifestations in conditioned reflexes has made it possible to confirm Pavlov's work by defining more accurately the circumstances surrounding the formation of conditioned reflexes. However, it will never be a dependable indication of cerebral activity. What we record is not the totality of electrical activity, but certain elements that can be diffused to the outside. This involves chiefly variations of polarization at the level of the surface processes of the pyramidal neurons, for the activity of clustered neurons such as the granule cells remains localized and is not diffused through the skull. For another thing, we are a long way from knowing how to use all the information collected. Our analyzers emphasize either frequency or intensity, which are two partial aspects.

It is therefore preferable, when possible, to record electrical activity directly in the brain, at the level of the thinking network. Even before 1939, such research, called *electrocorticography,* had been begun on animals. It remained fairly crude because the electrodes were large by comparison with the neurons and required serious operations, making it impossible to study a normal animal. It is in this area that the greatest progress has been made during the last decade. We now know how to make *microelectrodes* * with diameters of something like a thousandth of a millimeter, and we thus reach neuronic dimensions. We can, for example, depending on the place, distinguish the electrical activity of the various zones of a pyramidal

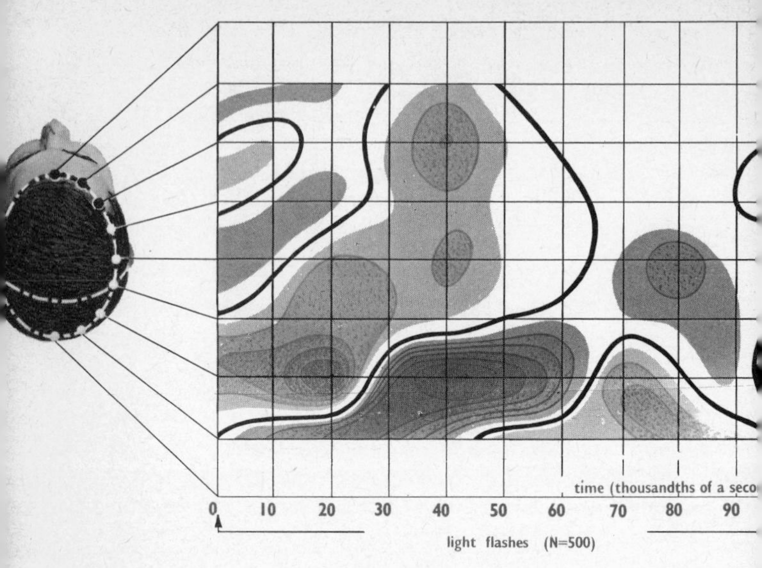

The electric activity of the brain. Charts by Rémond.

neuron: the dendrites, the cell body, the axon. It has even been possible to record the activity of the cellular nucleus. These electrodes can also be placed very precisely thanks to *stereotactic instruments (stereotaxis *)*, which are a kind of framework placed on the skull and possessing precise gradations making it possible to fix the electrodes and to

Blocking reaction: under the effect of excitation, the alpha waves are replaced by less ample and more rapid waves.

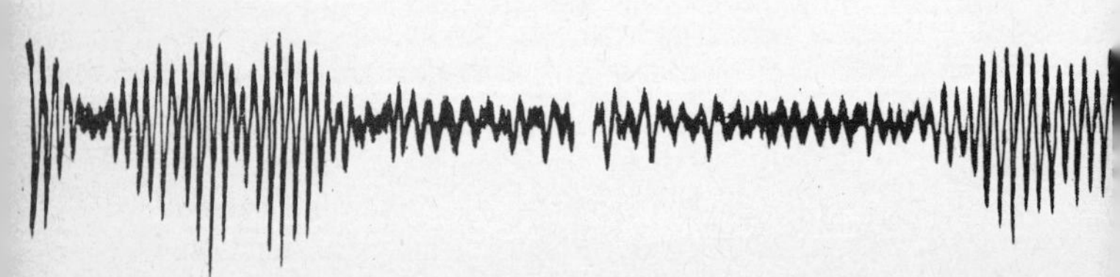

Taking an electroencephalogram with multiple electrod
Ink recordir

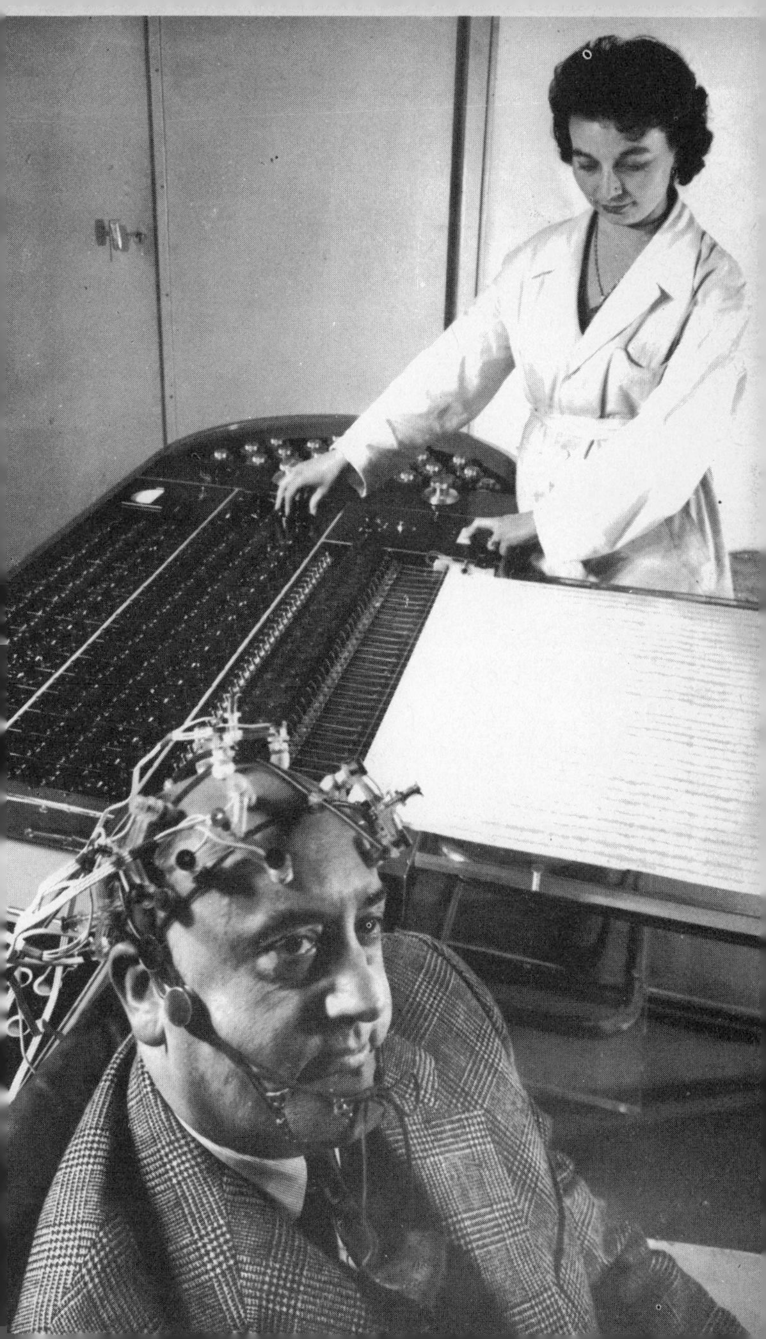

locate their position in the skull precisely. It is easy to verify at the autopsy where the electrode was.

Small electrodes are not disturbing. They do not injure the brain, which moreover is insensitive. They can be introduced by very fine trepanation openings made when the subject is anesthetized. One can therefore prepare an animal in advance by placing a series of electrodes permanently in its brain. It will thereafter live a normal life and, by connecting the electrodes with long, flexible wires to recording machines, one will know what is going on in the different parts of the animal's brain in the most natural conditions of spontaneous or stimulated behavior. A cat will walk about the room, drink, fly into a rage in front of a dog, lie in wait for a mouse, be stroked, etc. A monkey will earn a banana by choosing the knob of a particular color that it should press upon. One learns in detail what happens in the neurons at the time of the formation of a conditioned reflex. The issuance of a motor order or the reception of a sensorial message is recorded. There is thus created a whole new, precise physiological anatomy by the method of recording *evoked potentials.* * (By this term we mean the electrical activity that is created in a particular neuron by a distant excitation in any part of the body or the nerve centers.) We are beginning to know in detail the relations between the various sensitive cutaneous corpuscles and the various neurons of the cerebral parietal zone, as well as the connections between the various parts of the cochlea of the ear and the temporal zone. We are locating the zones of localization and the regions in which the messages from the senses are diffuse, or those where different messages converge on a single neuron. We are learning to recognize in detail the interrelations between the brain and the basal ganglia, the brain and the cerebellum, and the interconnections within the brain. We are coming to see that the actual physiology of an animal that is awake, conscious, and attentive is very different from that of a sleeping animal. For another thing, these same electrodes can be used to *send out* a weak electric current and to see how it will disturb cerebral functioning. With a brief, intense current, we produce through electrocoagulation a local lesion, the effects of which will be known immediately. These actions do not merely modify

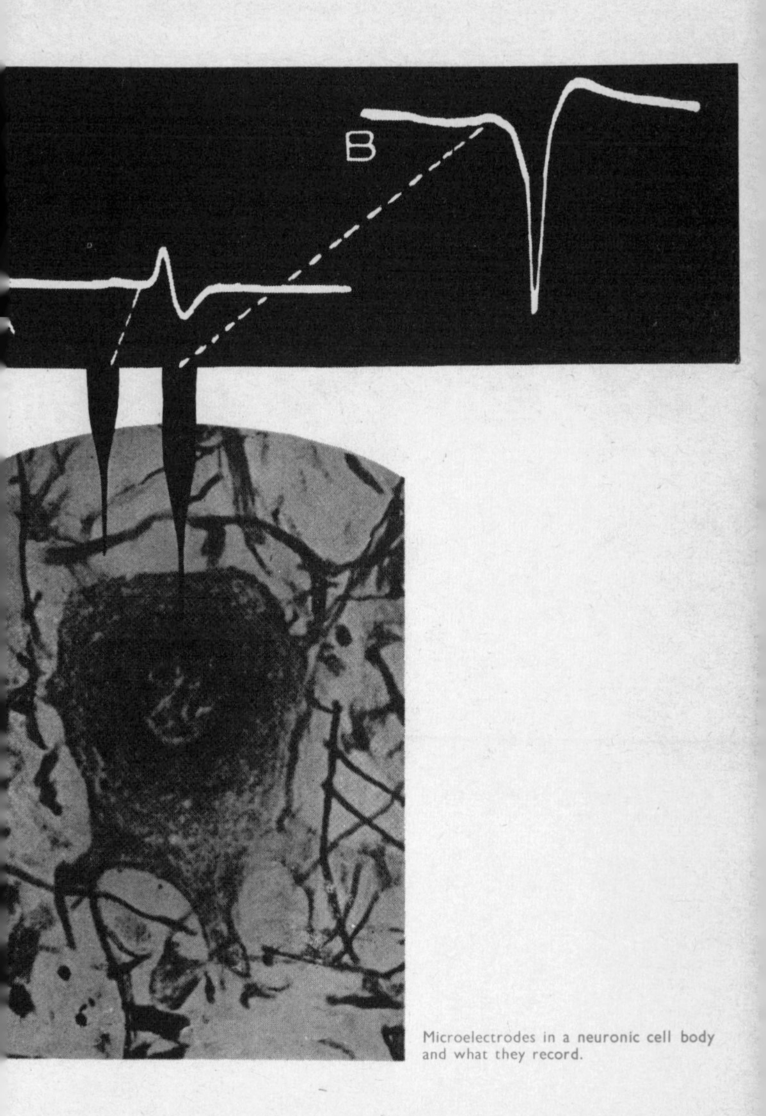

Microelectrodes in a neuronic cell body and what they record.

Studying the cerebral reactions of a cat at work.

spontaneous behavior; they can also *create certain kinds of behavior,* activate the animal. By means of excitation or localized lesion, one can cause repose, put to sleep, create an exaggerated and pointless activity, make felt a need to eat or to care for the young or satisfy this need, calm or create a rage. One can also reverse reactions: certain excitations or lesions result in a cat's being happy and purring when it is hurt, or becoming angry when stroked. A monkey through whose prefrontal region a current is made to pass no longer knows how to solve a problem it has learned. It no longer knows what knob to push in order to get the banana; it abandons the banana for peanuts and takes it up again when the current is turned off; while the current is on it allows itself to be stroked, but as soon as the current stops, it bites. A rat either accepts the presence of a mouse or kills it, depending on the state of its brain. When electrodes are placed in certain regions, electrical stimulation is so pleasant that the rat can learn to stimulate itself intensely by pushing a knob.

There has thus been created a whole science of *behavioral neurophysiology*, which was relatively crude in the past, being limited to the external study of animals that had been operated on and were seriously mutilated – deprived, for example, of the prefrontal region. It is becoming more and more precise, increasingly involving normal subjects. Pavlov's refusal to be satisfied with a psychological explanation (the animal's wishes or desires) has led to an understanding of what happens physiologically when the animal wishes or desires. With Pavlov, neurophysiology had given up the oversimplified materialist dream of finding the mind or spirit in the brain. People no longer paid attention to anything but physiology (paths, reflexes, nervous impulses, excitations and inhibitions). Consciousness seemed to be eliminated from the physiologist's preoccupations. But the end result of this experimental effort has been, as it happens, the creation of a physiology of consciousness. We are beginning to understand how the cerebral mechanisms make consciousness and thought possible.

And it is not just animal consciousness and thought that are involved. All these methods apply to *man*. This is not

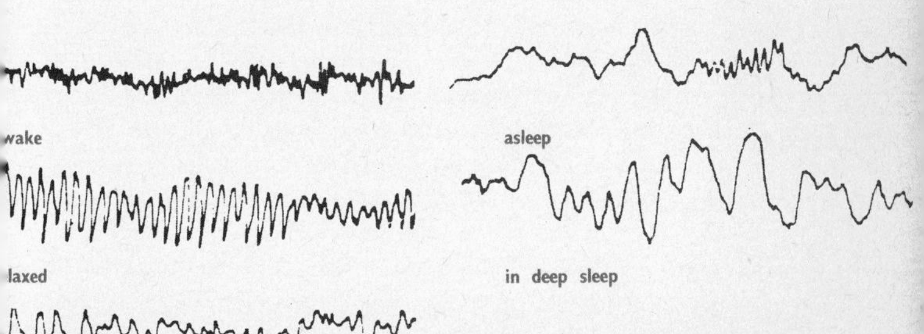

From wakefulness to sleep.
Progressive slowing-down of the cerebral waves.

to say that he is made to undergo unreasonable experiments for the sake of increasing our knowldege. But, for necessary therapeutic purposes, the operating room of the neurosurgeon has become a real laboratory of human neurophysiology. Even before operating on someone, as soon as it seems likely that the operation will take place, it is necessary to test the state of the brain exactly, to locate the diseased zones. During the operation, the surgeon must know which zones to respect. Finally, certain operations constitute real experiments involving precise cerebral destructions *(lobotomy *)* on carefully examined mental patients in order to improve their condition. Moreover, we have gradually learned to make the destruction proportionate to the patient's condition. A study of the psychism after the operation is profitable to psychophysiology.

Thus in men it is not only, as in the case of animals, the active, behavior-directing brain that is studied by means of microelectrodes, but also the brain as the organ responsible for human subjectivity and reflective interiority. The patient who is awake (whose being awake, moreover, helps the operation) and who does not suffer can not only show by his behavior the consequences of what is done to his brain, but also tell you what he feels. Conversely, we can observe the cerebral aspect of the states of consciousness he describes to us. Communicating with him by conversation, we can get him to perform certain acts and have certain thoughts, and we can then see what goes on in his brain. We can also see how, by acting upon his brain, we modify his behavior, his thought, his consciousness, and his will.

This formidable possibility of molding a man's mind (we shall return to this subject) assuredly represents a marvelous source of progress in our knowledge. Here are some examples. Excitation of the motor zone does not seem to be volitional; the subject does not feel that he is responsible for the movement he makes. Excitations of sensorial zones cause hallucinations. In a region located between the occipital lobe and the temporal lobe, electrical excitation revives real memories. The subject is convinced that a record is being played for him; it is the song his mother sang to make him go to sleep when he was a child. The electric current has created in his brain a certain architecture of excitations and inhibitions – not haphazard, but corresponding to a cerebral possibility that has existed – that is, a memory. This memory is indeterminate, for it has no specific connection with the excitant. The latter merely activates complex structures, since ablation of the excited zone does not suppress the memory. We are beginning to bring to light in the brain the complex structures that are the basis of memory. By exciting another zone in the region of the hippocampus we can prevent the fixation of memories from taking place. The patient forgets what he has done during the excitation; he has, that is, a disturbance similar to that in alcoholics.

The various language centers were known through the lesions of victims of aphasia. Then the neurosurgeon Penfield showed them to us in action. Their excitation has no effect upon the speechless subject, for the cerebral language structures are too complex to be created by the excitant, but the subject who can speak becomes aphasic, cannot speak, or stutters during excitation.

If we excite a region at the base of the brain, the patient declares that he is sleepy or becomes grouchy because we have touched the centers of sleep or of disposition. Lobotomy operations performed on the prefrontal region modify the personality by suppressing pathological anxiety. A dog that has been operated on in this way cannot remember an act it is about to perform if its attention is distracted.

When the brain is subjected to a rhythmic luminous excitation, loss of consciousness can result. This is what happens sometimes to a driver going along a road bordered by trees, with sunlight coming through them from the side. By exciting the brain with the theta rhythm, one causes manifestations of anger. The same methods enable us to know what is going on in the brain during momentary periods of real alienation caused by certain narcotics or stupefacients * such as mescaline or Mexican hallucinogenic mushrooms.

It is therefore out of a professional sense of duty, without metaphysical preoccupations, that the neurophysiologist today explores a consciousness which can no longer be called an epiphenomenon because it, too, is a cerebral phenomenon. The brain is different depending on whether one is awake or asleep, attentive or absent-minded. Consider the patient who has electrodes in his occipital white matter. The impulses arriving in the occipital zone are recorded while rhythmic flashes are being shown in his eyes. If we ask him to count the flashes, he is attentive; the impulses are very intense. If we distract him by asking him just any question – his age, his nationality – we immediately see an inhibition arise. The distraction causes a diminution of the sensorial message, because the neurons are no longer activated by *attention.* * It is not that the brain is less sensitive to these messages, but it automatically receives fewer of them because of the distraction.

These few examples show how modern methods during the last decade have revolutionized cerebral neurophysiology, truly raising it to the dignity of a science of human thought and consciousness. But hadn't the secret of the special quality of our brain already been penetrated by Pavlov, to whom language seemed to be a kind of conditioned reflex of a superior order that is made possible only by the complexity of the human thinking network?

Modern cerebral neurophysiology is a precise analytical and quantitative science. It is moving toward that scarcely imaginable goal of knowing everything that is happening at every instant in each of the billions of the brain's neurons. Such knowledge can be useful and profitable only if, following the advice of Claude Bernard, we do not forget that analysis is of no interest except in making us understand the *whole.* The whole in this case is the manner in which the *integration* of all the elementary cogwheels in the over-all functioning of the brain enables us to think and be conscious. Like every man, the neurophysiologist is endowed with introspection; but it is his duty not to limit himself to the microphysiological analysis of cerebral functioning considered by itself. He must try to understand how this cerebral functioning enables him to be conscious and free. This is not a question of philosophy, but of neurophysiology's own progress toward an understanding of man.

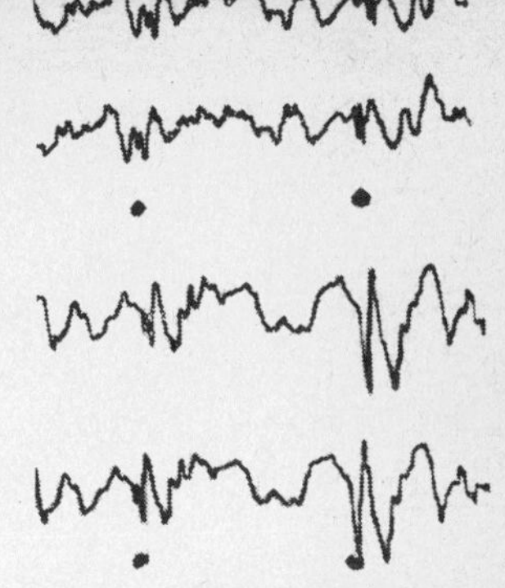

The impulses reaching the mind of a man are more intense when he is counting flashes of light (below) than when his attention is distracted by such a question as "What is the name of the President of the Republic?" (above). The black dots indicate the flashes.

We can today, therefore, record directly an objective indication of neuronic excitations and inhibitions – their electrical aspect; we can also create them and disturb them. Anyone who could analyze and integrate the electrical phenomena of all the neurons at every instant would know all the cerebral conditions of psychism. We are, admittedly, very far from being able to do this, but even if it became possible, it would not in the least result in the destruction of psychology, which deals with the psychism by itself or as manifested in behavior. The beauty of a woman lies entirely in her material conditions: the features of her face, the softness of her skin, the brightness of her eyes. All this can be analyzed and measured objectively, and yet nothing takes the place of direct knowledge of this beauty.

The thinking network is the seat of two types of electrical manifestations: unpropagated fluctuations of the neuronic electrical charge, which are an index of the state of excitation or inhibition, and nervous pulsations, which are waves of nervous impulse, transmitting nervous messages along nerve fibers. Waves that are relatively large (several millivolts) and fast (50 to 100 meters per second in the case of the large myelinized fibers of the "life of relation") were the first to be known. Adrian analyzed the sensorial message in which the intensity of the excitant increases the number of fibers involved as well as the frequency of impulses in each and the motor message in which these same factors condition the intensity of the response directly. More modern research has shown the existence of slow, unpropagated variations of surface polarization which precede or follow the wave of nervous impulse. Such slow waves exist at the level of the cell body, which has a surface charge that varies according to the multiple influences that work upon it: innumerable impulses arriving rhythmically at all the synapses, modifications of chemical origin resulting from the effect of the moods on nervous chemistry, and the direct effect of the neighboring electrical field of the other neurons. When the depolarizing effects prevail, the neuron is excited and sends into its axon multiple nervous pulsations; when the superpolarizing effects prevail, it is inhibited and slows down or suppresses its emission of impulses. The cell body thus brings about the integration of everything that concerns it and deduces the suitable response. Whereas nervous pulsations play an important role in transmission at a distance, a large part of local functioning in the cortex is thought to depend on the relaying of waves of polarization and depolarization from one to the next without the obligatory intervention of waves of impulse. As a matter of fact, the interesting thing about electroencephalography is that it gives us information – unfortunately only partial – about a certain aspect of the synchronized and desynchronized fluctuating pulsations, while electrocorticography records both oscillations of polarization and propagated waves.

The great secret of the *harmony* of cerebral functioning lies in the fact that the excitations and inhibitions are not haphazard, but are distributed according to a variable organization adapted to what is required, so that incoming impulses are switched in such a way as to be used best, and motor orders are born.

This harmony depends on the *good condition of the neurons,* which are not passive conductors, but living cells reacting to the extent that they are in good physiological condition. Although the nerves have a rather weak chemical dynamism *(metabolism *),* this is not at all the case of the centers and the cerebral cortex, the organ with the greatest needs. This explains its great sensitivity to all disturbances of the inner environment. Among these needs is blood bringing enough oxygen, glucose, and varied aliments, and carrying away the waste products left behind by activity. There exists a complete *chemistry of the brain,* which is necessary for thought, not because thought is the result of this chemical activity but because the harmony of the nervous processes, from which thought originates, requires a good neuronic condition just as the filaments of the tubes

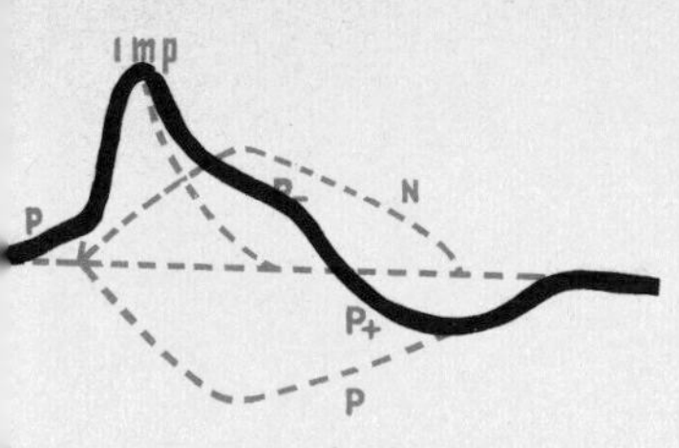

'he nervous impulsion (imp) is followed by nodifications in the electrical charge of the ıerve fiber, some negative (N) and others ositive (P). Modifications of excitability result: n above-normal phase (Psp) and a below-ormal phase (Ps) which follows the refractory eriod (P.R.), which is absolute at A (unex-itability), then relative at R. Before the im-ulsion, there are preliminary variations in he charge (p).

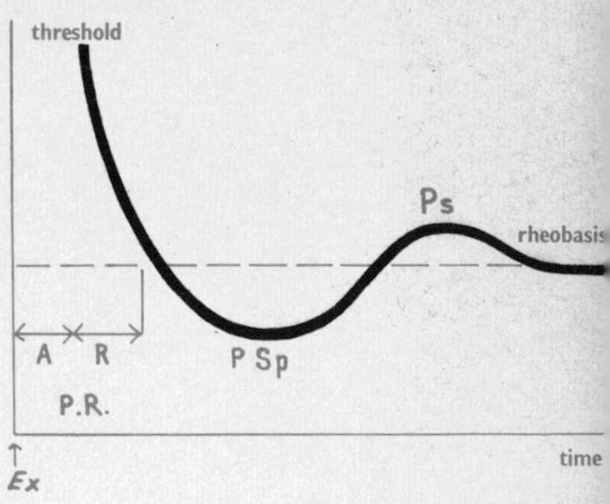

of an electronic machine must be heated correctly. States of cerebral disequilibrium may have as their origin an apparently insignificant alimentary disturbance such as a vitamin or hormone deficiency or excess, resulting in pathological * behavior, pseudo-faults or vices for which the patient is not responsible.

For functioning to be harmonious, there must be such a distribution of excitations and inhibitions that the propagation of waves of polarization and impulses will occur as needed. Now, this propagation, which depends on processes of self-excitation, is conditioned by the excitability of the neurons, their sensitivity to the effects that work upon them. There exist *physical* laws of propagation: it takes place best between matched elements that are capable of being in resonance, and the more excited the elements are, the more active it is. Propagation and in particular synaptic transmission does not rely exclusively on the direct electrical, physical action of polarization and the accompanying wave of impulse. *Specific chemical* processes are also present. The electrical activity of the nervous system involves the release of chemical substances which play an essential role in the processes of excitation and inhibition. These chemical processes, the second aspect of the brain's chemistry – not heating the filaments but sending out impulses and switching them *(an essential operation of thought)* – are fairly well known for the sym-

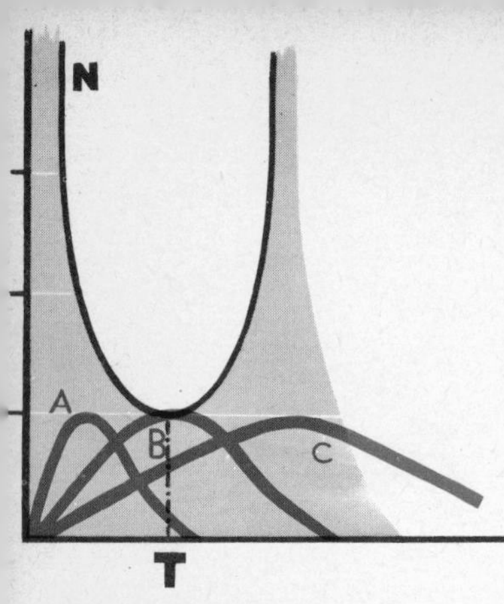

Efficacity of the impulsion, depending on its duration. On neuron N, only impulsion B, whose duration coincides with the time needed T of N, will be efficacious. Impulsions A, which is too short, and C, which is too slow, will have no effect.

pathetic peripheral command of the visceral effectors. They are much less well known in the brain, but a great deal of research these days shows the importance in cerebral harmony of such *chemical mediators* * as adrenaline, * acetylcholine, * their derivatives, serotonine, * etc., and their possible role in mental pathology. Some of these studies are very promising from the therapeutic point of view.

If the switching and issuance of impulses are made in accordance with needs, it is because the thinking network is a *self-regulated* * system, like a modern machine that controls itself. This teleological explanation should be considered by the biologist independently of any philosophical position. After all, it is no more astonishing than the admirable harmony of anatomical structures. This anatomical harmony, which is the result of embryological construction, has the task of making possible correct functioning, without which the organism could not have survived.

Cerebral self-regulation possesses a triple aspect. The first regulation is the one that the impulse *exercises upon itself* merely as a result of the fact that it circulates within the anatomical organization of the thinking network. It thus creates processes of excitation and inhibition that open up certain paths to it and close others. Convergence and divergence of the neuronic circuits reflect the fact that the impulse does not move in a straight line along rectilinear paths following successive neurons, but that it irradiates in a network with multiple links including backtracking. All this modifies excitability in various respects. The neuron is unexcitable during a brief period after the passage of the impulse *(refractory period *)*. It undergoes fluctuations of excitability – excitations and inhibitions – just before and just after the impulse, so that the succeeding impulse will never find the neuron in the same condition. The connections established by embryological development are such that the alternation between excitations and inhibitions resulting from the routing of the impulses will be adapted to what is required, whether it is a question of innate kinds of behavior or of the possibility of grafting new kinds of behavior (conditioned reflexes resulting from cerebral coexistence of signals during training).

But, as we have seen, it would be a mistake to think of the switching of a single impulse or of a single sensorial message with multiple impulses in a brain at rest. The new impulse is going to be *integrated* in a complete nervous interiority, in a brain that is the seat of multiple nervous switchings originating in all the sensorial messages constantly coming to it. There will accordingly not be simply an automatic switching of the message. It is going to enter a brain possessing a certain type of excitations and inhibitions upon which it will act, and this will influence its type of switching and use. So it is, for example, that in the motor cerebral cortex as well as in the spinal cord, the motor neurons of antagonistic muscles *(extension and flection)* are not in an equivalent state. One of the muscles is always in a state of tension opposed to that of the other. Its own sensitivity continually originates regulatory messages that give information to the motor neurons. The neuron of a stretched muscle is therefore in a different state from that of a relaxed muscle and it will react differently to an impulse. It is by interaction between two nervous processes that the coexistence of two signals makes possible the establishment of a conditioned reflex. Awareness itself depends on the integration of a partial nervous phenomenon in the over-all functioning of the brain.

However, these local self-regulations in the cerebral cortex are not enough to explain the harmony of nervous functioning. There exists an *over-all self-regulation,* depending on a regulatory device located outside the brain and ensuring its good functioning. It was the physiology of *sleep* that first gave us an idea of it. After observations by Von Économo of lesions at the base of the brain of subjects who had died of encephalitis lethargica (1919), there gradually developed the notion of centers of sleep and waking capable of stopping or activating all cerebral

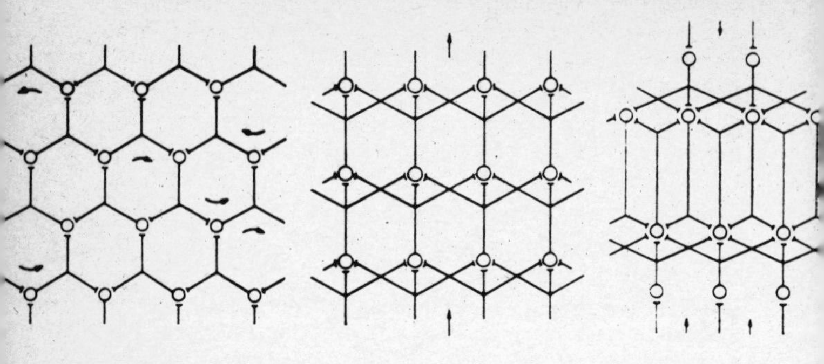

Diagram of nervous connections. The thinking network.

functioning. It has been possible to cause sleep or insomnia, in animals or in men, by varied excitants, particularly electricity, and by lesions.

From the biological point of view, sleep is *necessary repose* for the brain, without which it would become poisoned by the chemical waste products of its ceaseless functioning, as has been shown by the researches of Piéron and Legendre involving experimental insomnia resulting in a dog's death: the cerebrospinal fluid then contains a poisonous *hypnotoxin.* * But, normally, one falls asleep before becoming poisoned, and in order not to be poisoned. Sleep becomes a need and an instinct; it enables us to avoid tiring the brain too much, by stopping its functioning in time. It is a protective anticipatory mechanism that could be associated with the greater susceptibility to fatigue of a sleep center at the base of the brain. This center is thought to be located in the region of the instinct centers and near the regulatory centers of muscular tonus and sympathetic equilibrium. This would then explain why sleep is not merely a cerebral inhibition but has a somatic aspect – that is, the loss of muscular tonus which makes it necessary to lie down and the general slowing-down of the "life of nutrition." In 1941, the notion of a sleep center became a particular case of the general regulation of nervous functioning. We have pointed out that, in a normal subject, nerve chronaxies vary under the effect of the centers. This phenomenon of subordination depends on a *regulatory center* located in the base of the brain; it is therefore responsible for the harmony of the alternation between excitations and inhibitions in the wide-awake brain. Sleep results from the functional blocking of this center, which deprives the cerebral neurons of an activating and integrating influence and plunges them into inhibition, homogenization, and disorganization, and it is this which accounts for the incoherence of dreams (P. Chauchard, 1941).

It is such a conception which has prevailed today over theories that made of sleep a purely cortical process. Since 1949 and the fine researches of Magoun and Moruzzi, the apparatus of wakefulness has been known anatomically and its functioning explained. There exists in the base of the brain, from the medulla to the mesencephalon with extensions in the hypothalamus and the diffuse system of the thalamus, a *reticular formation* * – diffuse gray matter formed by a rich network of small interconnected neurons. They receive through the collaterals of the great ascending paths of sensitivity numerous messages, nervous impulses of sensorial origin that will not have an informative role (sensation) but an activating one. They contribute toward developing the reticular formation's special activity, and it in turn activates the cerebral cortex. The fatigue of this formation blocks impulses in it, bringing about in return a deactivation of the brain, which, no longer having enough impulses to keep up its activity, slips into inhibition.

Moreover, there exist interactions between the brain and the reticular formation, which explains, for example, why we can go to sleep at will. But the reticular formation does not have only this awakening action. It is the center that is charged with ensuring the specific reflex self-regulation of the activity of all the neurons, placing them beforehand in the required state of excitation or inhibition. This center, which is very sensitive to any variation in its inner environment, is today the object of innumerable researches. A general awakening action on the cortex is not its only function. It is also responsible for that specific kind of wakefulness that is called attention, the corollary of which is an inhibition of distraction, an elective sleep in regard to what one does not pay attention to. It is this

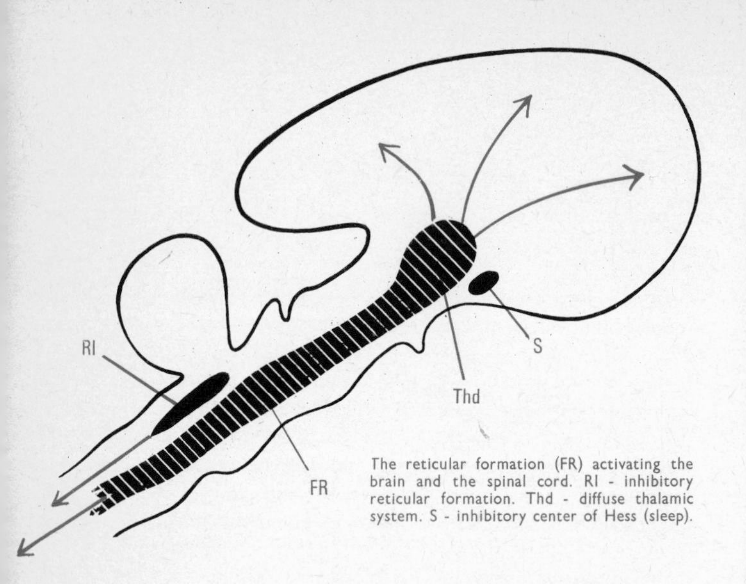

The reticular formation (FR) activating the brain and the spinal cord. RI - inhibitory reticular formation. Thd - diffuse thalamic system. S - inhibitory center of Hess (sleep).

self-regulatory apparatus that is responsible, for example, for the inhibition of visual impulses we have spoken of in a patient whose attention was distracted. This inhibition of distraction involves even the corresponding peripheral neurons.

Like Pavlov, people believed for a long time that conditioned reflexes involved only the cerebral cortex. Today it is recognized that the basal centers and particularly the reticular formation play an important role in their formation, either by commanding the desired regulation or by providing the new interconnections at the appropriate level.

The Brain and the World

At the point which we have now reached, our knowledge of the cerebral organ is sufficient to enable us to understand how the activity of the human thinking network explains our possibilities of thought and consciousness, even though this activity depends on fairly simple material phenomena, the consequence of the chemical dynamism of living matter. Indeed, except for the complexity of the network, nothing distinguishes the human brain, the organ of true mind, from the animal brain or from a center whose activity is purely automatic, such as the spinal cord. When complexity is low, the corresponding activity of the center provides *no more than an interior.* The more this activity grows in complexity and becomes autonomous, the more it tends toward interiority. *The psychological dimension is the other aspect of the material organic dimension.*

But, before approaching the cerebral mechanisms of thought and consciousness, we must first consider two more elementary functions of the brain: the genesis of *sensations* * and the command of actions.

Sensation is usually considered as an elementary state of consciousness and cerebral action is identified with will. Actually, it is necessary to distinguish between two phenomena of different orders which represent distinct cerebral functions. Sensation is, on the one hand, a cerebral state

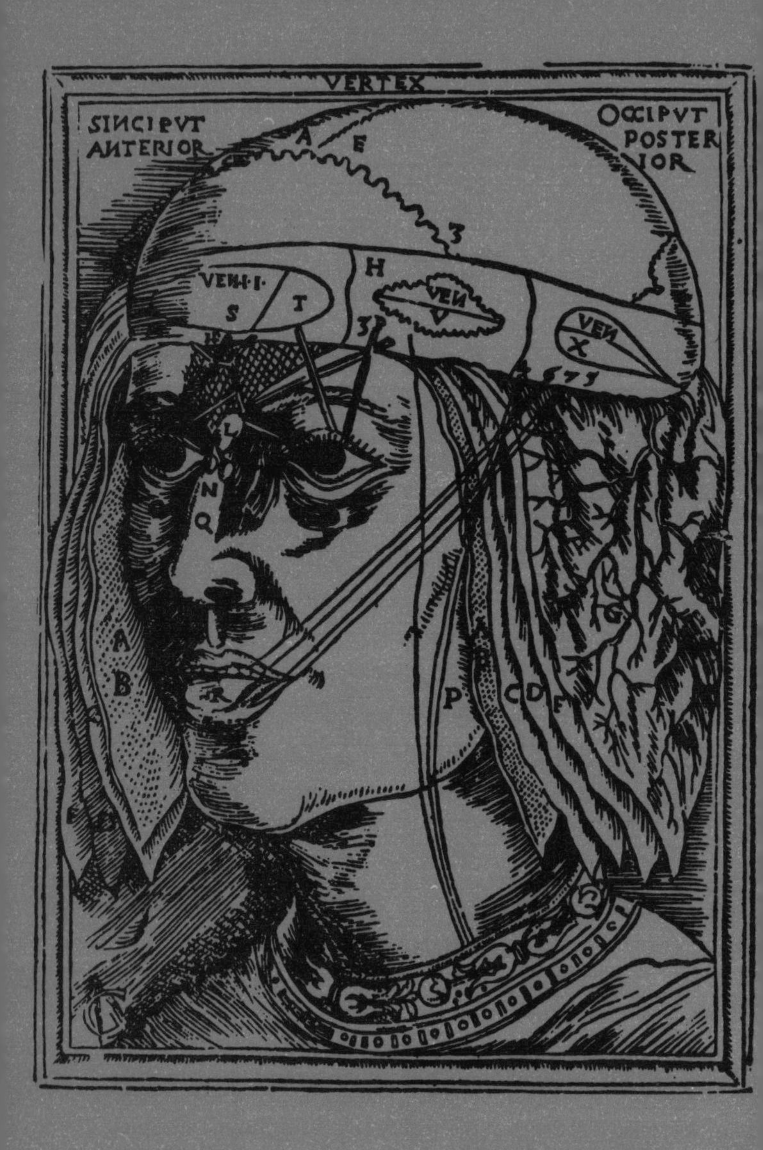
VERTEX
SINCIPUT
ANTERIOR
OCCIPUT
POSTER
IOR
VEN·I·
VEN
VEN

which, by itself, is unconscious, a kind of "pre-sensation," a transposition of the world and the body into cerebral structures thanks to messages from the senses that reach the sensorial structures of the brain. On the other hand, there is the awareness of this cerebral state, which will produce the true sensation with all its effectiveness in reflective conduct. Similarly, will is the taking charge by the individual consciousness of the cerebral motor mechanisms, though the latter can function automatically, independently of the will.

Sensorial knowledge

The physiology of sensations is one of the principal chapters of experimental psychology. It deals with sensations in themselves either as states of human consciousness felt by a subject who tells about them or, more objectively, as sources of a kind of behavior that proves what has been felt, even in the case of an animal. In addition to the rat that enjoys stimulating itself, modern *psychology* offers us the experimenting pigeon pressing its beak on knobs to equalize two luminous intensities in order to earn an alimentary reward. Actually, such physiology is experimental psychology. The real physiology of sensations, like the physiology of cerebral motoricity, should look for the organic and more particularly the cerebral mechanisms that make sensations and movements possible.

Scientific psychologists have been completely right in affirming the necessity of an objective study of sensations and actions apart from any reference to consciousness and will. But this is a first analytical level of experimental research. It does not mean that consciousness and will are exclusively metaphysical values. We shall see that they also have an objective aspect accessible to science in the study of the personalizing integration functions of the brain.

The functions of sensitivity

Spread out over the surface of our bodies in the skin, muscles, and tendons, or located in special sense organs – the retina of the eye, the cochlea of the ear, the taste buds

The brain and its relations with the body (sixteenth century).

of the tongue, the olfactory zone of the nose – are innumerable sensory receptors specialized in various kinds of sensitivity to the outside world necessary to our behavior. They make possible what are usually called our five senses: touch – with its information of a mechanical, thermal, and painful nature – sight, hearing, taste, and smell. Everything that becomes sensation, which is born only in the cerebral cortex in human beings, depends on what has made an impression on our senses and on the way in which this *unconscious impression* has been transmitted to the brain by the nerves, the central bundles, and the nervous structurations, with their various neuronic relays. An ideal integrating apparatus could thus construct successive stages of impressions preceding sensation involving the peripheral level (the state of excitation or inhibition of the receptors) and the nervous level (the ensemble of all the sensorial messages – successions of electric impulses of variable frequency) with its modifications in the various centers, the last of which before the cortex is the thalamus – the relay and power station of the automatic integration of the sensitivities (except the olfactory, which goes directly to the brain). One thus sees both what there is about the sensations that is objective, because they correspond to an external phenomenon, and everything that is subjective: the way in which our senses are sensitive only to certain aspects of reality and in an incomplete and unfaithful way, the difficulties of transposing different processes into a single electrical code, and the deformation of this code in the course of its ascent toward the brain in successive relays.

Cerebral reception, which transforms the electrical code into a mosaic of excitations and inhibitions – the cerebral aspect of sensation – introduces an additional subjectivity. Fortunately, in men and the higher animals, the brain is not only a source of illusions because of habits; it is above all, because of its ability to compare, integrate, and abstract, the origin of a return to objectivity. Thus is born in men scientific objectivity as well as the mathematical vision of the world, thanks to this desensualized human cerebral coding, whose effectiveness confirms its validity.

In this analysis of what precedes sensation, we must write more specifically about the special case of the eye, in which the retina is a true nerve center and accordingly possesses an elaborative and integrative power over visual impressions that is much superior to that made possible by the ear, in which the receptors are independent. The retina, which has numerous interconnections, behaves like the spinal cord.

But the realm of sensitivity goes far beyond the classic five senses. The eye is not only sensitive to light; it is also an organ of palpation at a distance, giving us information about space and relief, thanks to the sensitivity of its muscles. The ear is not only an auditory organ; the sensitive corpuscles of the utricle, the saccule, and the semicircular canals inform us about positions and movements of the head in space, while the sensitivity of all our muscles, tendons, and articulations enables us to know the position of the various parts of our body. The *sense of space* is a sixth sense.

Of the inside of our body, we normally feel nothing; nevertheless, it contains numerous sensorial receptors, sources of nervous messages that ensure harmonious functioning without our being consciously aware of them. At the level of the neck, the bifurcation of the carotid artery contains a true sense organ, the *carotidal sinus*, which is very sensitive to pressure and the amount of oxygen in the blood; it establishes corrective reflexes that defend the alimentation of the brain. In pathology, certain of these internal messages become conscious in the form of severe pains (stomach burns, various colics) or of pains transferred to a corresponding cutaneous zone.

Finally, there exists another type of sensation of internal origin – sensations of *need* * They are numerous – hunger, thirst, need of evacuation, the sexual need, the need for sleep, the need for rest, and the obscure sensations of well-being or indisposition. All these needs also depend on the arrival at the cerebral cortex of informative messages of internal origin.

Messages from the senses have other roles besides the informative one of creating a cerebral perturbation that will produce a sensation. They are, first of all, at the level of the lower centers, the source of innumerable reflexes ensuring functional harmony. If we stand erect and keep our balance as we move, it is because the sensitivity of

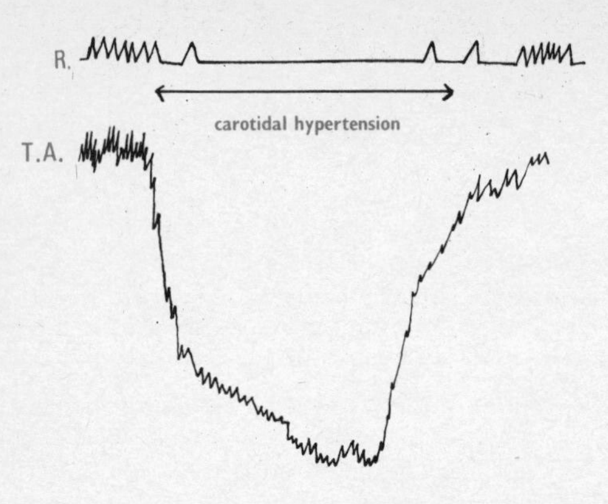

Unconscious internal sensitivity.
Regulation of arterial tension by the carotidal sinus.
Hypertension sets off a hypotension (TA) and suspended breathing (R).

our muscles and the sense of balance of our inner ear automatically provide a self-regulation of muscular tonus at the level of the medulla, the pons, the mesencephalon, and the cerebellum. The proportion of these impulses going to the cortex to provide sensations is relatively small.

But at the level of these centers of the base of the encephalon, messages from the senses have two other unconscious functions of capital importance. We have already seen their role in the *awakening* of the brain thanks to their nonspecific convergence on the reticular formation. For another thing, they are the agents of *innate kinds of behavior,* both instinctive and affective, whose center is the hypothalamus. In this case the sensorial messages are not informative, but purely and simply *signals that evoke* a type of behavior. Modern study of the instincts * (Lorenz, Tinbergen) has shown that they can be reduced to chains of successive reflex kinds of behavior, analogous to conditioned reflexes, in which the animal does not judge the situation but is successively sensitive only to certain signs of the environment, all of which makes it possible to induce behavior by artificial lures. The motor neurons of the hypothalamus can become co-ordinated in such a

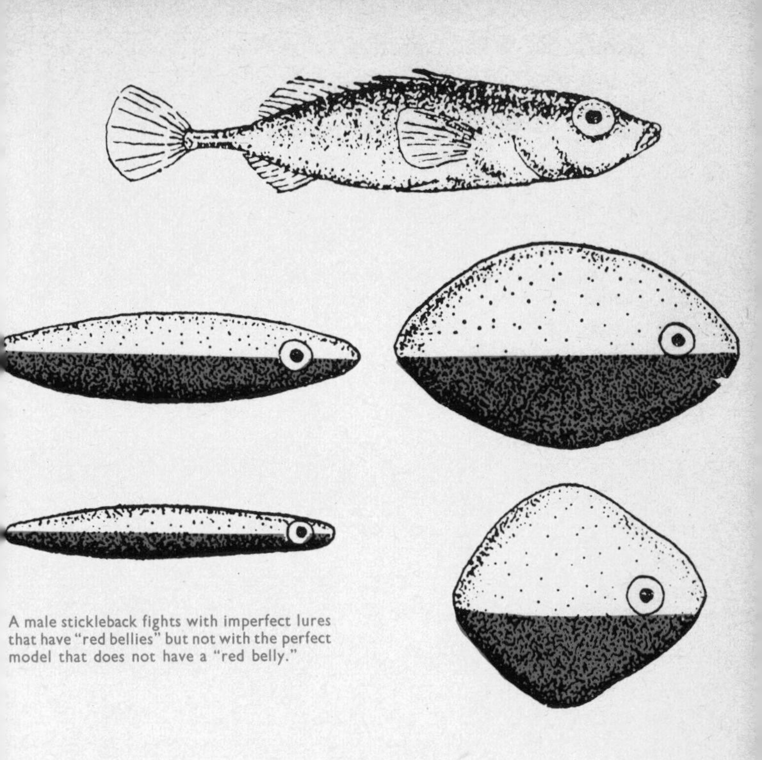

A male stickleback fights with imperfect lures that have "red bellies" but not with the perfect model that does not have a "red belly."

way as to provide extremely varied kinds of behavior – alimentary, sexual, etc. The type of behavior is determined by a hypothalamic modification such as the action of the sexual hormones. Organic manifestations of the lack of nourishment cause such modifications by direct reflex action. If the disturbance is very strong, the behavior is *spontaneous* (a pigeon that coos); if it is weaker, it *activates* the animal (appetitive behavior) which, by moving about, will find in its environment factors to appease its nervous modification. This modification makes it sensitive to certain sensorial signals that will set off a certain kind of behavior, and this process will bring about a temporary return to repose. Such are the automatisms of hunger and sexual need. We have purposely described them without using any psychological vocabulary, for at this level the need is unconscious; the sensation of need is generated by the repercussion of the hypothalamic disturbance on the cerebral cortex, and it is made precise by the direct awareness of certain local organic modifications (epigastric sensations in the case of hunger, dryness of the throat in the case of thirst). This sensation will lead to completing the instinctive behavior by a voluntary effort and to being able to master it more or less; on the other hand, the brain, out of habit, will multiply the evocative signals, causing artificial needs.

Among these hypothalamic disturbances that produce in the brain a diffuse, nonlocalized agitation, which is the source of this very special type of need sensations, *affective* manifestations must be considered separately. Indeed, this *affectivity,* * which seems to us to be essentially conscious, is only secondarily conscious, like all needs. States of surprise or interest, pleasure, pain, * or anger are specific nervous states of the hypothalamus, and consequently unconscious automatisms disturbing the whole organism in a reflex way. What is involved is an individual's innate equipment causing him to act only if he experiences an unconscious pleasure in acting and to draw away from what is harmful only if it makes him feel displeasure. It is therefore only subsequent to the hypothalamic disturbance that the subject is conscious of his affective state. The brain, by conditioned reflexes, develops the factors of affectivity considerably. In an innate way, except for certain situations, these affective states are chiefly dependent on certain peripheral messages such as those of pain or pleasure (caress, sensual enjoyment). Great pains (or rather their organic cause) and sexual orgasm are first of all unconscious hypothalamic *shocks* * before becoming conscious as they agitate the cerebral cortex. Here also, there will be two types of sensations in the cortex: a diffuse one depending on the effect of the hypothalamic state on the whole brain (that is, pain and sensual pleasure taken by themselves), and another one that is localized thanks to the cortical sensorial receptors, the seat of pain and pleasure.

As we have pointed out earlier, all this utilization of the sensorial signals in the behavioral basal centers is possible in men (as it is impossible in cats or dogs) only because of the cerebral cortex. It alone awakens the basal centers sufficiently to enable them to respond to the sensorial signals, which retain their role as triggers of automatisms but in closer relation to cerebral reception, the source of sensation. For that matter, the person who does not reflect often uses impulses from the senses not as a source of information but as a signal for a conditioned reflex or a habit, forgetting to judge the over-all situation and to use his sensations fully. This is still truer in the case of certain neuroses. * Consider a robin fighting with his rival's red feathers on the end of a stick and neglecting the nearby rival who has been deprived of this "evocator." What is more comparable to such a robin than the neurotic fetishist who indulges in sexual activity with a woman only if she has a special pathological evocator, which may be any common object connected with the history of his neurosis?

What characterizes man is the decrease of what is innate and the increase of what is acquired in the satisfaction of his innate needs.

Cerebral sensorial localizations

Let us leave the subject of diffuse states of need and deal with the cerebral bases of precise informative sensations. How, thanks to the senses, does our brain know the world and distinguish us from it?

Formerly all that was known was what amounts to real cerebral sensorial organs made up of the neuronic networks of the various lobes in which the paths of sensitivity finally terminate. Today we know, because of the method of evoked potentials, that at multiple points of the cortex there also arrive more diffuse messages coming from the senses, often with a convergence of different senses on the same neuron. This is the case with the primitive brain, or rhinencephalon, in which there exists no sensorial localization but which is reached by numerous sensorial messages for the higher regulation of the instinctive and affective life. In the rest of the organ, studies on the wide-awake brain provided with its regulatory apparatus have shown the multiplicity of sensorial receptions outside the specific zones. The latter seem to be a special case whose role is a precise, informative one based upon the arrival of the message by rectilinear ascending paths with few relays, whereas the other messages are thought to have a role that is both activating (awakening) and regulatory and to come from messages that have been diverted by the reticular formation.

We possess in our brain *sensorial zones of precision* connected point for point with the peripheral receptors. This *somatotopy* of construction (the development of the various lobes of the neocortex is in proportion to sensorial and motor functions) finally creates automatically, through messages from the senses in the cerebral network, structures of excitation and inhibition which represent the cerebral aspect of the peripheral impression. These are therefore partial aspects seized by our various senses and they are such that our senses dissociate the peripheral impression of the outside world and of ourselves by analysis. Because this is the anatomical point where the paths from the senses terminate, any lesion in such a precision apparatus, anatomically localized and incapable of being replaced, will cause a loss of conscious sensitivity localized in the corresponding point; that is, insensitivity of such-and-such a cutaneous zone, of such-and-such a part of the retina, etc. An electrical excitation, for example, will cause a sensorial hallucination: the brain will interpret any artificial excitation of the sensorial zone as if it came from a normal impression of the sense organ. We recognize this in the case of human beings by their reported impressions. In the case of animals, certain manifestations show it. For example, exciting the parietal tactile region gives the impression of itching and the animal scratches the corresponding cutaneous region.

We are accustomed to recognize occipital excitations as light and excitations of the temporal auditory zone as sounds. If we could connect the auditory nerve to the visual paths, sounds would create luminous impressions;

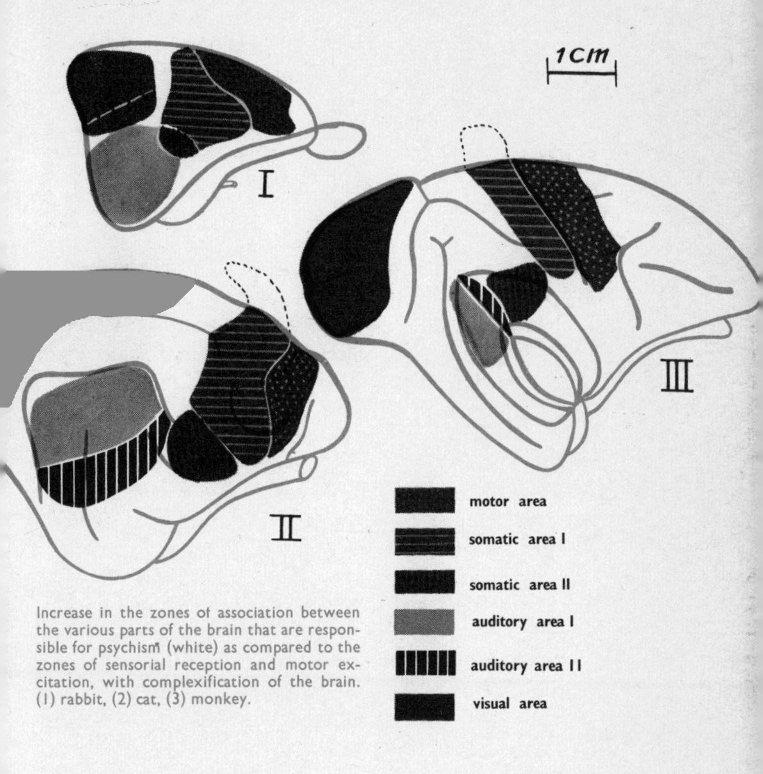

Increase in the zones of association between the various parts of the brain that are responsible for psychism (white) as compared to the zones of sensorial reception and motor excitation, with complexification of the brain. (1) rabbit, (2) cat, (3) monkey.

an educative correction would no doubt intervene subsequently. In this way a blind person can discover light when his auditory nerve is excited. Thus, by placing an electric circuit permanently under the skin near the auditory nerve, Djourno was able to make deaf people hear in a certain way by learning how to code the sounds, which are transformed into an electric current that excites the internal circuit from a distance by induction. Similarly, light (phosphenes) is the name we give to the effects of shocks on the eye or electrical excitations of the optic nerve. Numerous illusions are thus possible. Certain chemical substances such as peyotl mescaline have the power of causing colored hallucinations by exciting the cerebral visual zones. The visual notions of up, down, etc., depend on the habitual relations between certain retinal zones and our brain. If one changes conditions by turning the eye 180 degrees (which is possible only on a toad) or if one makes a monkey or a man wear prismatic glasses that have an analogous effect, reactions are reversed: what is in reality on top seems to be on the bottom. Monkeys and men adjust to this, but toads do not; instead, they hurl themselves toward the ground to catch a fly in the air.

Thanks to cerebral sensorial localizations, the outside world and our bodies are no longer exclusively external and objective things; they become *cerebral states,* reflections or images – that is, *subjective* manifestations of our interiority. Normally, we objectify the cerebral state by relating it to corporeal or external reality. But the cerebral structure has become, through habit, a relatively independent reality, and this is why we can mentally evoke a particular object or a particular part of our body, not because they are exciting our brain at the moment, but because we remember them and can use our imagination to arouse in our brain the cerebral structuration that they had formerly created there. The prototype of this purely cerebral activity, detached from the messages of the senses, is the dream.

These cerebral images extend far beyond the mere zones of sensorial reception and involve an immense extent of the brain. Actually, the zone of sensorial reception provides, in an innate way, by the play of anatomical connections and their activation by sensorial messages, the simple cerebral transcription of analytical sensorial impressions – that is, the cerebral aspect of elementary sensations: touch, light, color, sound. All our knowledge will depend on these sensations, which exist first in the brain. One does not really educate one's sensitivity, but one learns how to interpret this cerebral image better, to distinguish its details better, and to give it a meaning. What is innate are the elementary sensations and one's cerebral aptitude for integrating them in a synthesis. This synthesis itself will be acquired in the course of a kind of training and will consist of the acquisition, thanks to the repeated coexistence of certain sensations, of conditioned reflexes that will give us the notion that distinct sensations belong to the same object. One moves then to the stage of perception, which is recognition and understanding of the over-all meaning of a series of sensations belonging to the same sense or to different senses. We are then less aware of elementary sensations and concern ourselves only with the synthetic image. This training of sensitivity occurs very early, even before the awakening of full consciousness, when the child playing in his cradle learns how to recognize things and the parts of his body.

In technical language, these conditioned reflexes which enable us to integrate various sensations in order that we may make use of them are called *gnosias.* * They do not depend directly on the neuronic circuits of the sensorial zones; it is the neighboring regions which are anatomically predestined for this task. One can, therefore, also localize the gnosic centers; their lesions cause disturbances of a special kind, a loss not of sensitivity but of interpretation. One sees light, one hears sound, one touches a hard, cold, and pointed object, but one can no longer say what this object is or what this light and this sound mean. The most characteristic example is the well-known linguistic agnosia: *verbal blindness* in someone who sees letters but can no longer give a meaning to the words, *verbal deafness* in someone who hears but no longer understands the meaning of language. Agnosias relating to each sense are localized. The further one gets from the reception center, the more complex become the hallucinations produced in the gnosic zone by the cerebral excitation. For example, where vision is concerned, as one moves away from the tip of the occipital lobe, one moves from simple phosphenes – sparks of light – to a more and more elaborate vision of shapes and objects. The complete cerebral image of an object requires the confrontation of the partial images of the various senses, the association of the various parts of the brain. It is therefore no longer either localized or in danger of disappearing because of localized lesions. The zone of sensorial reception is very closely connected with the neighboring gnosic zones; the farther one gets from the gnosic zone, the more numerous become the connections with parts that are far away from the brain. Formerly, there was a tendency to locate in the gnosic zones real storehouses of images, the material seat of memories. Today a dynamic representation is substituted for this static view: the gnosia is a special type of structuration of the excitations and inhibitions among thousands of neurons of the thinking network, bringing into play the interconnections and regulations of the basal centers of the brain.

Another problem presented by these sensorial receptions is that of a single reality which is projected in two hemispheres. Of course, the two hemispheres are linked by numerous interconnections, particularly the fibers of the corpus callosum; nevertheless, good harmony requires one of the two to have the dominant, *directorial* role. Indeed, conflicts between hemispheres are at the origin of many nervous and psychic disturbances. This is what happens when a left-handed * person, whose dominant hemisphere is the right one, is obliged for social reasons to use his right hand predominantly, especially for writing, thereby imposing a directorial role on the left brain; many psychosomatic disturbances result, particularly stuttering. Stuttering may also result, according to Tomatis, from a lack of balance between the two ears, one of which becomes the directing one.

Receiving centers and gnosic centers exist on both sides. The former are divided according to anatomical connections that often include crossings. Thus, in the case of tactile sensitivity, the parietal region receives everything that comes from the opposite side. In the case of the ear, the con-

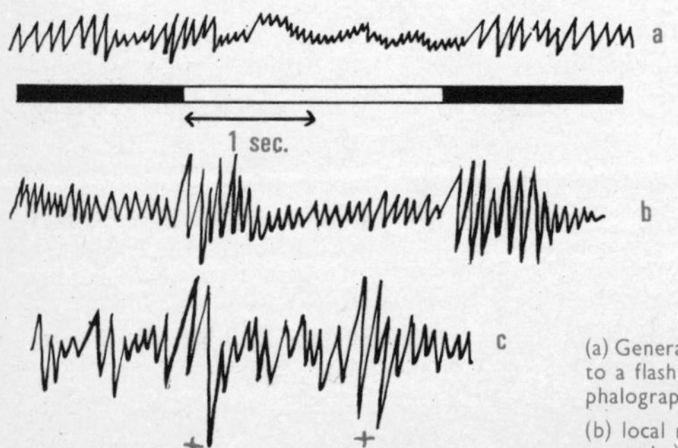

(a) General response of the brain to a flash of light (electroencephalography).

(b) local response (electrocorticography): effect at beginning and end.

(c) local response of the auditory zone to two shakes of a rattle.

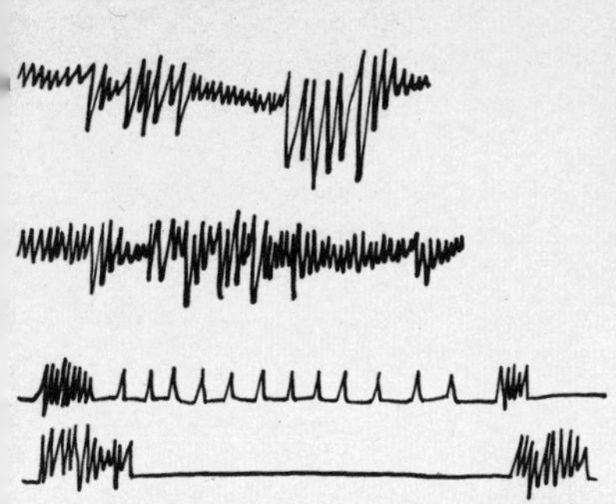

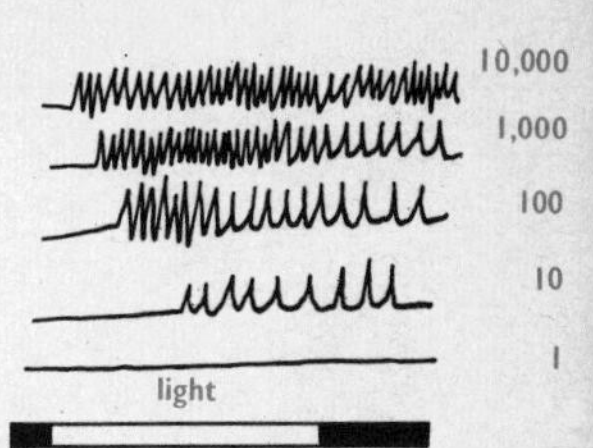

Sensorial messages. Above: a - response of an alligator's auditory nerve to the word "Bonjour." b - response of the vestibular nerve of a tortoise to the animal's being turned around. Below, left: response of three kinds of fibers of the optic nerve of the king crab. Right: response of the same nerve to an increasingly bright light.

nections are bilateral: each temporal lobe is linked to both ears. In the case of the eye, each *fovea* (the central part of the retina, serving precision sight and color sight: the zone of fixation) is connected simultaneously to both tips of the occipital lobe, but each hemisphere on the edges of the calcarine fissure of the inner surface of its occipital lobe receives the impulses of the opposite part of the visual field – that is, what has made an impression on the temporal peripheral half-retina of the same side and the nasal half-retina of the opposite side; the upper fourth of these zones reaches the upper lip and the lower fourth the lower lip of the fissure. This accounts for the modalities in cerebral lesions of partial losses of the visual field, or *hemianopsias,* * as shown in the illustration on page 106.

Although the gnosic centers are bilateral, pathology shows that the functions of the two sides are different. It

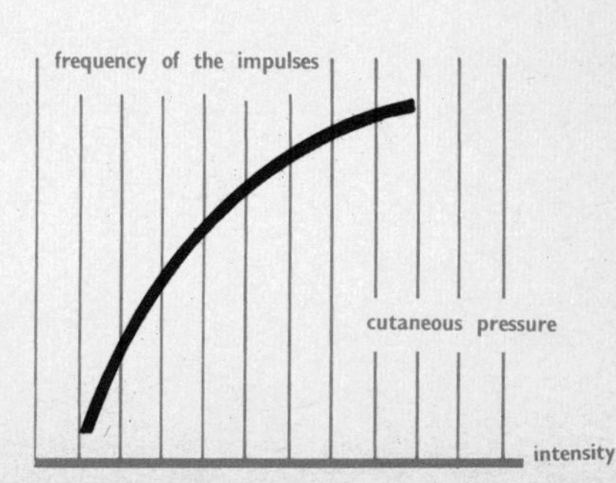

Sensorial message. The frequency of the impulses increases with the intensity of the excitant.

is above all in the domain of linguistic gnosias that dominance is clear-cut: these gnosias are located on the left in a right-handed person and on the right in a left-handed person. Only lesions on this side disturb language, and from this point of view ablation of the opposite hemisphere makes no difference. The dominance of the brain hemisphere controlling the right hand when the right hand is favored is easy to understand. What is more obscure is the reason for the dominance of this hand in most men and women.

What does one localize in the brain as regards sensorial information? Behind the fissure of Rolando, the ascending parietal convolution is the cerebral *image of our body.* * This is where all messages of general cutaneous, muscular, and internal sensitivity arrive. We have there in the brain, in the form of cerebral structures, the equivalent of our whole body with its parts and organs. The image is not accurate; since all the parts are not equally sensitive, they cannot claim a cerebral surface proportionate to their

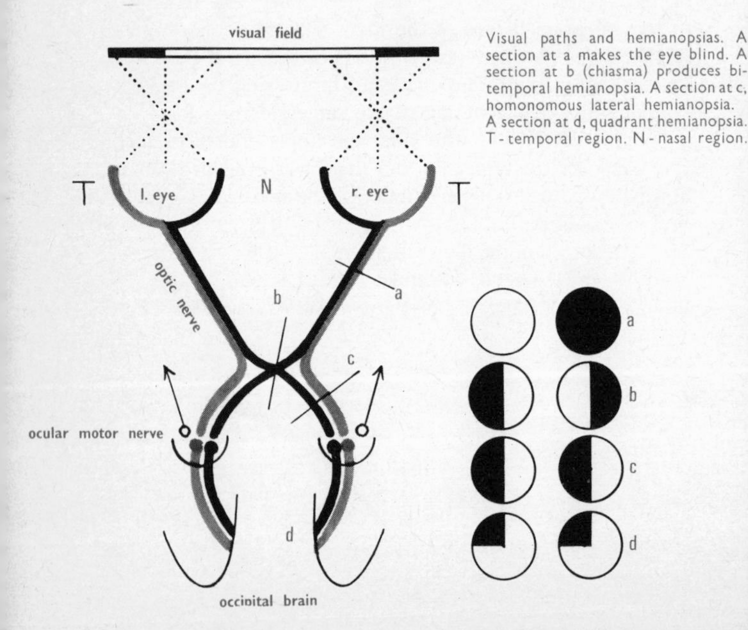

Visual paths and hemianopsias. A section at a makes the eye blind. A section at b (chiasma) produces bitemporal hemianopsia. A section at c, homonomous lateral hemianopsia. A section at d, quadrant hemianopsia. T - temporal region. N - nasal region.

peripheral surface. A drawing of ourself based upon this image would be grotesque: huge feet near the top on the inner surface, small legs and a small trunk on top, large upper limbs with enormous hands and giant thumbs, large face with an important zone below for the tongue, the throat, and all the sensitivities of the phonatory organs.

Modern studies are beginning to give us the details of this organization. Every point of the skin is connected with several specific vertical neuronic columns of the various cutaneous sensitivities. The various points have cortical zones which overlap, but precision is achieved by means of phenomena of neighboring inhibition. This zone also receives the unconscious visceral messages, though in smaller quantity. This explains how they can sometimes reach consciousness in the pathology of pain or intervene in dreams. One thus understands the closeness of psychosomatic relations and the possibility of suggestion in the unconscious visceral domain. Finally, *gustatory* sensitivity has its seat in the general sensitivity * of the tongue, but like visceral sensitivity it also sends many messages to the various parts of the primitive brain.

This analytic image of the body becomes significant in the gnosic integrations made further back in the lower part. These parietal gnosias make possible the sense of touch and palpation, thanks to which we recognize objects; they also give us the sense of the position of the parts of our body. They co-ordinate the sensitive messages of the phonatory organs, of which most people, with the exception of singers, are not very conscious, and they are the seat of a *vocal corporeal schema* (Soulairac) of a sensory image of the sounds and words of language.

In man, exciting this region, which is a real sensorial center of language, causes temporary aphasia. But, above all, the parietal gnosia established in childhood is a true presence of ourself in our brain which provides us not only with an on-the-spot means of distinguishing between ourself and the external environment along with the objects that touch us, but also with the permanent notion of the self and the non-self, of objects, and of other people. This *image of our body,* which depends above all on general sensitivity, is considerably improved and completed by the contribution of the other senses: sense of balance of

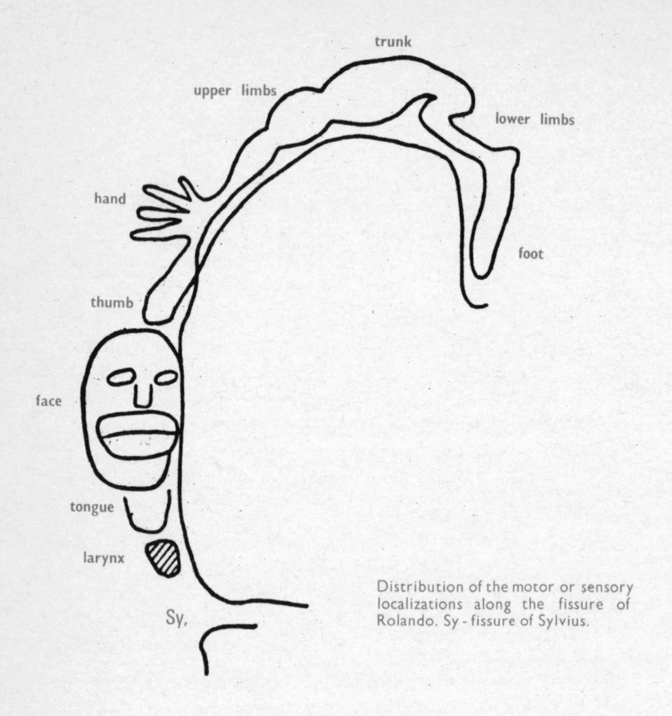

Distribution of the motor or sensory localizations along the fissure of Rolando. Sy - fissure of Sylvius.

the inner ear which, by the semicircular canals, gives us the three dimensions of space; auditory sense of space; visual sense of space; vision of ourself, of objects, and of other people. The gnosic zone's being centrally located at the parieto-occipito-temporal crossroad makes it well suited for this synthesis. Another aspect of sensorial messages places us in, and gives us the sense of, *time*.

In addition to partial agnosias such as the inability to recognize objects by the sense of touch (called *astereognosis),* the more serious disturbances of the corporeal schema must be placed in the parietal regions. This diagram subsists in amputees, who accordingly have the illusion of possessing a phantom limb, sometimes a moving or painful

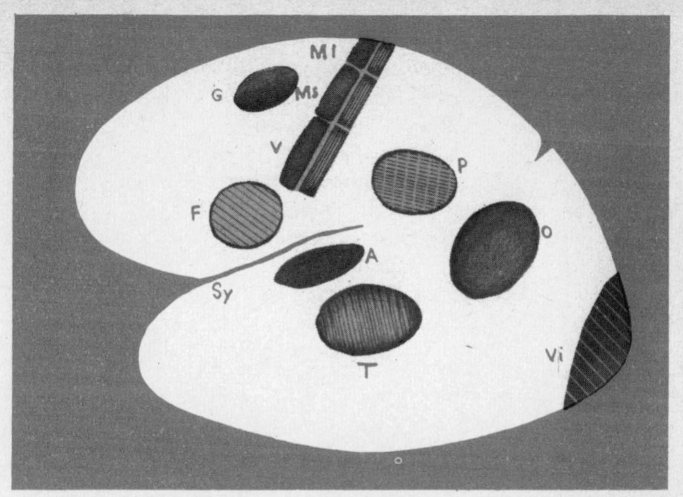

Language centers. Left brain of a right-handed person. V-motor center of vocalization. F-center of verbal articulation (motor aphasia). G-center of writing movements. P-sensorial center of language. A-auditory center. T-center of the audition of words (verbal deafness). Vi-visual center. O-reading center. Sy-fissure of Sylvius. Mi-lower limbs. Ms-upper limbs.

one. Certain paralytics lose the notion that their sick limb belongs to them. Finally, in psychiatry, there are cases of mistaking the image of oneself for a double (positive *autoscopy* *). This is Musset's "stranger dressed in black who resembled me like a brother," or the agonizing disappearance of one's image in a mirror, described by Maupassant.

In accordance with the strict localizations that we have pointed out, the occipital zone is a real *cortical retina* in which are transcribed the visual image of the world and the visual sense of space. Central vision is preponderant in it because each cell is connected directly to the brain (which accounts for precision vision), whereas the further one goes toward the periphery of the retina, the more numerous are the visual cells connected to a single central neuron. On the outer surface of the occipital lobe, the gnosic zone provides visual perceptions and the possibility of reading.

As for the temporal lobe, it has a *cortical cochlea* and here the localizations corresponding to the various points of the whorls of the cochlea make it possible to record separately the various frequencies of sound. Low frequencies are received in places different from high ones. We know today that this cerebral tonal localization does not correspond to an equally strict localization in the ear. It is inhibitions in the nerve centers at the level of the relays of the auditory paths that gradually provide a selective localization. Because of this localization, the brain can use for sound the rhythm of the impulses and the number of fibers involved, though more for the notion of loudness than of frequency. Indeed, in this case, the frequency of the impulses is ambiguous, because it indicates both loudness and frequency, the indications of frequency being fairly unreliable because of the nerve's being unable to follow high frequencies of sound. It is therefore necessary that an exact discrimination between frequencies be made possible by precise anatomical connections. Near this zone of sensorial analysis, the gnosic zone reconstitutes the sound by synthesis and makes it possible to recognize spoken language or music. The circuits of the gnosias are sufficiently selective that in pathology one can have, independently, varieties of verbal deafness and varieties of musical deafness, or "amusias."

As for the olfactory area, it is situated in front of the primitive brain, at the point where messages arrive in the brain. The whole sensorial brain, which co-ordinates the foregoing zones and ensures complete recognitions, calling upon all the senses, includes essentially all the lateral and posterior neocortex as well as the parietal, occipital, and temporal lobes and their connections with the basal centers, and finally the primitive olfactory brain, which is specially connected to the temporal lobe and the central lobe.

The action brain

Although, except for certain idealist philosophers, no one doubts that sensations correspond to objective phenomena, we are convinced that sensations are states of consciousness, that they are part of our interiority. On the other hand, volitional motoricity seems to us to be above all a control of muscular contractions, and therefore a process that is exterior to the brain, being merely set off by it. In reality, in motoricity, the muscle is only a means of execution and the brain is not the seat of a mysterious will. It will appear to us as the essential organ of motoricity. Bodily movement is not first of all its actual muscular realization; it is first of all a *cerebral motor image,* an internal preparation for action very comparable to the cerebral image of sensation. The classical opposition between thought and action, between *homo faber* and *homo sapiens,* is artificial because the cerebral structure is analogous in both cases: the technique and the instrument are first of all thought, first of all cerebral structuration. They are in the head before being put into action. People are too much in the habit of opposing physical education and mental education. One should speak of physical education only if it is a question of obtaining the muscular hypertrophy of certain wrestlers or monstrous "Apollos." On the other hand, there exists a kind of real *psychophysical* education, the art of using one's brain for the good exercise of motoricity; consequently, a good cerebral education in this domain is valid for the other, more mental aspects of cerebral education.

Behind the frontal lobe, in the frontal convolution that follows the front edge of the fissure of Rolando, we have a *motor image of the body* modeled on the sensitive parietal image. This is the seat of the pyramidal motor neurons to which the name psychomotor is applied (motor area). There are neurons, if not for the various muscles, at least for the important functions (flection, extension) of the various parts of the body. These neurons send their axons directly to a point of contact with the peripheral motor neurons in the spinal cord or the nuclei of the cranial nerves of the opposite side, and it is through them that they act upon the muscles. The importance of the cerebral control of a particular part of the body depends on the extent to which its motoricity can be made more precise. Therefore we find once more in the cerebral schema the same disproportion as in the case of sensitivity; the grotesque little figure can be drawn in the same posture and with the same look. The relations between the two zones are, moreover, very close. A bodily movement depends on a certain distribution of contractions and relaxations between numerous synergetic and antagonistic muscles. It involves therefore both cerebral structuration of excitations and inhibitions in the motor zone and sensitive structurations induced in the parietal region by muscular sensitivity.

Thus, wishing to make a particular bodily movement and getting ready for it means imagining the corresponding cerebral structure, which is both parietal sensitive structure and frontal motor structure. The parietal structures depending on peripheral messages are self-regulating, and prepare the motor zones in advance for possible action from a given position. In particular, there exist close relations between the centers of sensitivity of the vocal organs and the centers for the transmission of impulses, which are also located in the lower part.

As in the case of sensitivity, one finds less abundant motor neurons in their topographical place for visceral transmission of impulses, which however are not volitional. These neurons act only indirectly through the hypothalamus upon the *sympathetic system.* * One can thus understand that in conditioned reflexes or emotions, the organism participates in reactions as the "life of relation." All our viscera are present in our brain. Training such as that of yogis makes it possible to control them almost at will.

The psychomotor neurons of the frontal lobe region next to the fissure of Rolando are the agents of *precision movements;* they are therefore extremely important, but their importance must nonetheless not be overestimated. They are not the will, but an important cogwheel at its command. Their functioning is volitional only if the structuration is made knowingly; otherwise, it is a case of a pure cerebral automatism of which we can be secondarily conscious but for which we do not assume responsibility. For another thing, the lesion of these centers does not cause paralysis, unlike the lesion of the sensorial receiving centers, which brings about total anesthesia (except for diffuse pain). Automatic motor behavior can depend on lower centers such as the corpora striata or the hypothalamus; and there are other cortical motor neurons.

The excitation of this zone produces only small elementary movements, not significant ones. For example, excitation of the vocal center can produce an inarticulate cry. Significant movement requires the harmonious co-ordination of the functioning of the preceding executive neurons. It is the neighboring neurons located in the regions just in front of the frontal lobe region next to the fissure of Rolando *(premotor area)* which because of their connections possess the innate ability to co-ordinate the preceding neurons in such a way as to produce meaningful movements. But such movements are learned. A young child in its cradle creates for itself the conditioned motor reflexes of movements – that is, it learns how to graduate its various muscular contractions with skill in terms of the act to be performed, whether this be gripping or speaking. The premotor zone is therefore the seat of the motor structures, the image of the movements, particularly of those vocal movements which are the signals of language. They are called *praxias.* * The lesion of this zone does not paralyze but makes one *apraxic,* incapable of executing movements one has learned. In particular, the lesion of the lower part makes one a victim of motor *aphasia* * *(anarthria* – inability to articulate). Electrical excitation of this zone on a subject who can speak brings this about artificially.

When one observes in detail the motor activity of a subject who has lesions, whether of the motor or the premotor zone, one perceives characteristic modifications.

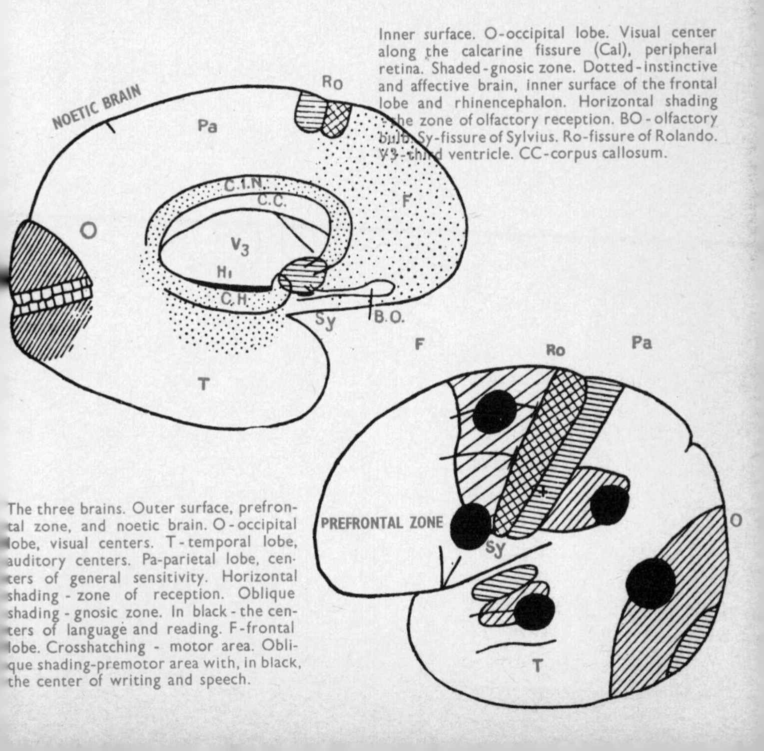

Inner surface. O-occipital lobe. Visual center along the calcarine fissure (Cal), peripheral retina. Shaded-gnosic zone. Dotted-instinctive and affective brain, inner surface of the frontal lobe and rhinencephalon. Horizontal shading - the zone of olfactory reception. BO - olfactory bulb. Sy-fissure of Sylvius. Ro-fissure of Rolando. V3-third ventricle. CC-corpus callosum.

The three brains. Outer surface, prefrontal zone, and noetic brain. O-occipital lobe, visual centers. T-temporal lobe, auditory centers. Pa-parietal lobe, centers of general sensitivity. Horizontal shading - zone of reception. Oblique shading - gnosic zone. In black - the centers of language and reading. F-frontal lobe. Crosshatching - motor area. Oblique shading-premotor area with, in black, the center of writing and speech.

What is involved is not a paralysis, but in one case a loss of precision, in the other a deficiency of total motoricity, accompanied in both cases by deterioration of the muscle tone. The reason is that, in addition to their praxic role of co-ordination of the motor neurons of precision, the premotor circuits also include motor neurons called *extrapyramidal* neurons which control the activity of the peripheral motor neurons, independently of the pyramidal neurons. In order to keep firm control over behavior, these peripheral motor neurons are the object of two higher commands: the direct control of the brain by the pyramidal path, and the control originating in the lower centers of automatic motoricity which utilizes extrapyramidal paths with complex courses involving numerous successive neurons. At the mesencephalic level, the extrapyramidal centers, which are subjected to the influence of the regulatory centers and the cerebellum, make possible postures and attitudes as well as the reflexes that enable us to keep our balance while moving. This involves a whole system of regulating motoricity in which the brain has no part but without which volitional action would be upset, as can be observed in the case of diseases of the cerebellum.

The patient with a diseased cerebellum cannot perform a succession of rapid and precise movements, such as those made by a puppet, for example; he is said to be afflicted with *adiadochokinesia.* * Modern studies have shown that for this kind of regulation, which is under the control of a precise volitional act, there are precise interrelations between the brain and the cerebellum. The latter automatically receives what amounts to the image of the act to be performed and it deduces from this an appropriate regulation not only of the peripheral neurons but also of the cerebral motor neurons – a precision regulation added to that of the reticular formation.

At the level of the base of the brain, this extrapyramidal motoricity initiates kinds of behavior that are not volitional. But this extrapyramidal path does not begin in the base; it also has its origin in the cerebral cortex, in the premotor area of which certain motor neurons are going to act upon the motor neurons of the corpora striata. This motoricity, unlike pyramidal motoricity, is an over-all motoricity, more all-inclusive and less precise. Thus, for harmony of bodily movement, it is necessary to have both the premotor praxic circuits and the participation of the extrapyramidal and pyramidal neurons, and meanwhile the lower automatic regulations play an essential role. Let us remember the crossed character of these cerebral controls, each motor area controlling the opposite half of the body. The praxias of language reside in the dominant brain.

These cerebral mechanics are controlled by the will, but can function automatically, just as sensation is in the brain even if we are not aware of it. But the more habitual and automatic a bodily movement is, the less obligatory for its functioning will be the cerebral motor mechanisms. They even reach the point of being able to depend only on the second motor level, the corpora striata. Normally, cerebral motoricity brings the motor areas and the corpora striata into close association. Contrary to what Broca thought, motor aphasia does not depend solely on the frontal zone but also on deep-seated lesions at the level of the corpora striata. There exists a whole hierarchy of motor levels. The automatic, unlearned motoricity producing walking depends on the most primitive part of the corpora striata, that which is the only one possessed by the lower vertebrates. Learned motoricity (swimming, etc.) depends on the new part of the corpora striata, that which developed at the same time as the neocortex and which works in association with it. The more automatic a learned act is, the more adequate the corpus striatum will be to take care of it, whereas the participation of the cortex is necessary for a willed, reflective act.

The motor cogwheels that we have just described are at the command of volitional bodily movement, an instrument of our psychism. But the brain can also control motor activity of another order depending on other motor cogwheels. We refer to *over-all kinds of behavior.* In this case, we are not dealing with circuits that are localized in different zones for various kinds of behavior, and the corresponding motor neurons of the extrapyramidal type have no localization but are distributed diffusely. However, electrical excitation thus reveals the possibility of varied reactions in the domain of the "life of relation" or of the viscera at numerous points of the primitive brain or of neighboring regions such as the central lobe. In addition, modern experimentation has made it possible to initiate or to modify complex kinds of behavior by excitation or localized lesion. Such is the effect of actions affecting the primitive brain or the prefrontal region. These zones are of the greatest importance for the automatisms of instinct and affectivity. What we have here is not a sensitive and motor brain, but a brain that regulates kinds of behavior thanks to certain more or less diffuse sensitive and motor elements.

The chief center of elementary instinctive and affective life is the hypothalamus, as opposed to the corpora striata, which preside over the automatisms of bodily movement. Just as the corpora striata are under the influence of the cortical premotor area, the hypothalamus is controlled by the primitive brain (rhinencephalon), which makes possible a much richer instinctive and affective life. The relations between primitive brain and neocortex place this activity under the control of consciousness and the will. Thus, for the exercise of action, the brain possesses two ways out. On the one hand, bodily movement: activity which belongs essentially to the "life of relation," at the level of the motor zones. On the other hand, complex kinds of behavior closely associating the "life of relation" and the "life of nutrition," an essentially psychosomatic path at the level of the primitive brain. From the motor point of view as well as from the sensorial point of view, the second path is further removed from full consciousness.

Thought and language

We have just seen two essential elements of what we have "in our head" – that is, in our brain: how sensorial messages, by automatically switching themselves in the structures of the brain, create there a representation of the world and of ourself that can be recalled independently of these messages, the structurations being partly innate and partly acquired; and how, for another thing, intracerebral activity can organize structuration to serve bodily movement and those varieties of behavior which are first of all a cerebral image before being motor execution. Cerebral impression that will be made into a sensation by our consciousness, motor image that our will can elicit – it seems that in dealing with these we are at a level of elementary mechanisms far removed from what is purely intellectual, from thought, from consciousness. We must therefore now ask ourselves if reflection on the subject of elementary cerebral functioning can give us an explanation of the organic bases of thought and consciousness.

The two levels of thought

When we meditate on our thoughts, we see first of all their most intellectual aspect – ideas with their abstract character – and we do not understand what connection they can have with sensory and motor cerebral structurations. In order to make the connection between cerebral interiority and mental interiority, one must first consider a more simple thought, such as thought in dreams, not because of its incoherence, which is connected with the state of the sleeping brain, but because it is thought by the association of images, a spectacle. One can also consider animal thought. Does an animal think? If by that we mean human thought, certainly not. But we now have objective indications that an animal is not an automaton whose activity could be said to be purely reflex. It does not guide itself exclusively by the signals of the moment, but also by what it has in its head. All the researches in animal psychology requiring an animal to learn how to orient itself in the complex maze of a labyrinth show that it orients itself in relation to what it knows, to the plan that it remembers. It is for this reason that an animal which knows a labyrinth immediately takes a short cut opened to it. The animal shows its intelligence by associating two past situations that it remembers in order to solve a new, more complex one. Pavlov was able to train dogs to have a succession of varied conditioned reflexes; each of a series of different signals in a fixed order would elicit a different reaction. If suddenly there came at a given time not the expected signal but a different one, it was nevertheless the reaction to the normal signal that was produced. The cerebral switchings were taking place according to an inner rhythm that had become independent of the signal; it had become, that is, a real thought.

Animal thought, the extent of which depends on the complexity of the brain, and the simplest human thought, which is much more complex because of cerebral progress, are thoughts by *images.* * We have seen how we learn to recognize objects, other people, or the parts of our body by associating all the partial cerebral structurations coming from the various senses. One thus forms a specific over-all cerebral structuration that represents and replaces the object and is the thought or idea of that object.

To think is to associate cerebral images (giving to the word "images" a general meaning encompassing more than sight) which the learning process has created in us, using messages from the senses as a starting point, and which, being evocable by the imagination, have become an internal code, an autonomous way of using our brain. The dynamism of thought, the succession of images, depends on the play of conditioned reflexes linking up the structurations to one another: for example, the fact that the image of a dog will remind us of everything we know about dogs or about a particular dog. There exists free association of thought; the images follow one another as in daydreaming or real dreams. But we can also control it, selecting at will certain images by directing our imagination. Just as cerebral sensory impressions exist independently of the attentiveness that makes sensations out of them, the unrolling of associations of images also goes on apart from what we pay attention to. There exists a whole system of unconscious thought going on inside us without our knowledge, the source of certain intuitions and certain rapid solutions of unsolvable problems.

Animals possess only this kind of thought by images, and in an elementary form. Thought that is distinctly human is situated on another level. It is a question of *verbalized thought,* of an *inner language.* * It is standard to define man by language, but language taken in its special quality as an intellectual process, as pure thought that is expressed, insofar as dialogue is concerned, in sensory and motor mechanisms. The profound difference between animals and men is said to be that the former have only a very simple language, a very affective means of alarm signaling, whereas in men language, which is very complex as a result

Cat operating a latch to free itself in order to look fo
food. It thinks with images, not with word

of the motor brain's greater ability to modulate sounds, is the means of expressing a thought independent of language itself. Language thus becomes a direct proof of human spirituality. The neurophysiological point of view is different: the greater complexity of the human brain does not merely give it the ability to emit much more varied sounds or to understand them; it makes of language, which is a means of communication, a new and more efficacious means of thinking. Man speaks, not because he thinks, but because his thought is an *inner language,* a human means of thinking. Language is not at the command of thought; it is first of all that thought and then its communication.

It was Pavlov who showed that language is a consequence of human cerebral complexity and that it objectifies the superiority and special nature of the human brain by comparison with the animal brain. He saw language as a special variety of conditioned reflexes, a *second system* of *signaling.* * The first system is that of the gnosias and praxias of direct thought by images. Education substitutes for each image its verbal denomination. Since he names everything, man is able, instead of associating images, to associate directly the corresponding names – a system that is better suited to developing the potentialities of abstraction of the human brain. To conceive by image the center of a circle is not so easy as naming it.

This possibility of naming comes from the fact that, since language is a special case of sensory-motor images, it can be detached from sensorial reception and motor command to become, as inner language, an autonomous cerebral reality. The image of an apple becomes the word apple. This word is both an auditory structuration (the heard word which we remember) and a sensorial and motor structuration (the image of the position of the phonatory muscles saying the word – an image which is partly parietal sensorial and partly frontal motor). Among civilized peoples, it is also the visual image of the read word, the motor image of the written word. Knowing the words of a language means taking them not only for sounds or ways of articulating, but as means of thinking; it means associating in one's inner language the partial sensory or motor structures of a word in an over-all structure. The word, which is a convenient means of thinking, remains at the same time a means of communicating one's own thought and receiving that of others.

Thinking by means of words becomes so automatic, for that matter, that we are no longer aware of it, unless we pay special attention. Since language is only a variety of cerebral images, it utilizes, like these, all the interconnected structures of the various sensorial and motor zones of the brain; the dominant brain is, as we have seen, preponderant. Whereas a localized lesion can disturb the understanding of spoken language or the possibility of articulating, the aphasiac, as a result of extensive lesions, more often than not has disturbances of his inner language that prevent him from manipulating the phonatory praxias. He can no longer pronounce words although he can emit articulated sounds. However, the aphasiac is not disturbed in his intelligence. True, this intelligence cannot get along without inner language, but what is disturbed is not the automatism of inner language but the voluntary evocation of words for dialogue, and so the aphasiac who is incapable of pronouncing a certain word will say it without difficulty in an automatism such as a proverbial phrase or an interjection. A mother may be unable to pronounce voluntarily the name of her daughter but may when the occasion arises call her automatically by name.

Grammatical relations – that is, the way in which we associate the words of language – are a functional modality of the human brain; from this point of view, progress in languages consists of a better employment of the brain's possibilities. Mathematical symbolism itself is merely a variety of language and therefore of cerebral signaling.

Innately, man possesses an aptitude for forming sounds that is manifested even by a deaf child, but he learns to use this aptitude in order to speak and think with the language of his environment, and this is why a deaf child cut off from his environment becomes mute. It is when a child begins to speak that he quickly surpasses a young monkey. However, it is not only the possibilities of speech that are involved here, but also the sheer cerebral maturation that makes this speech possible. A man who has not learned how to speak still has a way of thinking by means of images that is very superior to an animal's way of thinking by means of images. But man can realize all his potentialities only through language. The language brain is seen to be a real machine for thinking and reasoning logically. The originally communicative, motor character of language remains apparent in the fact that pure thought is accompanied by latent electrical manifestations which occur in the vocal muscles but are insufficient to activate them. In the case of a deaf-mute to whom a human inner language has been given on the basis of sign language, it is in the muscles of the hand that thought is manifested. We thus see how, thanks to the sensory-motor structures of language, a social, material, cerebral coding makes possible the intellectualism of the most abstract thought, in the same way as technical invention brings this about in modern calculating, guiding, or translating machines. The cybernetic comparison of the brain and these machines is very fruitful from this point of view.

The brain and consciousness

The brain is not only the organ in which our thoughts flow and where are located the mechanisms that enable us to feel and act; it is also the supreme organ of the person, the organ of awareness. The neurophysiologist leaves to the psychologist and the philosopher the task of studying consciousness in itself, but he cannot fail to take an interest in the cerebral conditions that make it possible. In the wide-awake brain, *attention* makes it possible to isolate certain phenomena which are in some way personalized *(personalization *)*, taken over by the subject who experiences them internally and judges them for what they are, either as highly significant sensations which he names or as actions. This attentive consciousness is not merely a passive spectator; it intervenes actively to direct cerebral activity, to recall images, or to voluntarily elicit acts whose value it judges, on a higher level, in relation to the individual's interest. Attentive consciousness thus becomes reflection and moral conscience. How is this transition, this jump, to be explained? How, thanks to the brain, can the subject rise above himself, move from passivity in the face of physiological determinisms to activity and responsible control, to *freedom* *?

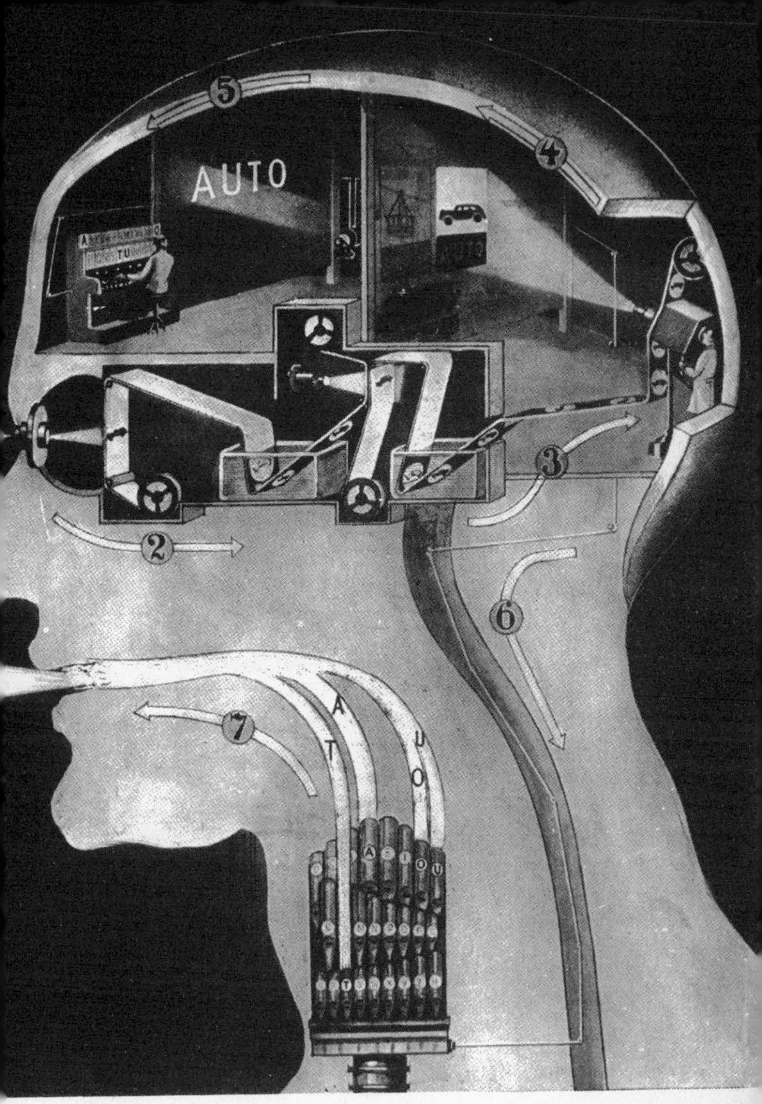

Everything is in our head.

For a long time these human values of consciousness and freedom seemed to belong to a purely spiritual realm. All that physiology was supposed to know about them was their limits, and so, in view of the importance of the determinisms that impose such limits upon us, some people reached the point of regarding freedom as an illusion. Today, on the contrary, the cerebral conditions of the free act are beginning to become clear. What characterizes the normal human brain, thanks to its complexity, is that it is *the organ which permits freedom.* It is the inadequacy of the animal brain that prevents it from rising far enough above determinisms to be able to direct them in a reflective way.

The brain should not be studied exclusively in an analytical way; one must also see what results from its harmonized and co-ordinated *over-all* activity. This is not because its total activity contains something other than the elementary processes revealed by neurophysiology, as *Gestalt psychology* * believed, but because the integration of these processes enables them to manifest new properties.

In order to be conscious, one must first of all be *awake.* Sleep is a loss of consciousness; we have seen its origin in that wave of inhibition which floods the brain when it is no longer activated by the regulatory centers of the reticular formation. Sleep is a protective physiological state that enables the brain to rest. It is therefore very different from all kinds of comas, which always involve a real poisoning of the brain. It differs from them in that cerebral activity is disorganized and slowed down but not blocked, as is shown by the example of dreams.

Although the messages from the senses no longer supply conscious sensations because of cerebral inhibition, they can nevertheless influence dream imagery. Unknown internal pathological irritations have even been revealed in this way by a premonitory dream. The subject dreams of stifling, for example, several days before having an attack of angina pectoris. It is upon this basis that certain experiments with *hypnopedia* (teaching or giving advice during sleep) have been made. The wave of hypnotic inhibition not only makes the brain less easy to activate, but also causes all active inhibitions resulting from wide-awake functioning to disappear. The subject is deprived of his defenses and is more suggestible. There exists a relationship between sleep and states of *hypnosis,* * in which the brain is also inhibited except in its relations with the hypnotizer. Hypnosis, which occurs fully only in certain subjects who are easy to inhibit, is neither a hoax nor magic; it is a kind of induced sleep. Certain *hypnotics* * given in weak doses bring about a state of somnolence which has been used therapeutically to suppress repressions, which are factors of psychosomatic disequilibrium. They have been popularized under the rather false name of *truth serum.* *

But being awake is not enough to make one fully conscious; *attention* is also required. Consciousness is seen to be a narrow beacon that lights up only a small part of cerebral functioning. We have seen that modern neurophysiological research tends more and more to place the physiology of attention in the forefront. Attention is seen to be a state of super-vigilance that includes an excitation of what one observes and an inhibition of what one is not paying attention to, as the result of processes of self-regulation that have their seat in the reticular formation. A cerebral process attracts one's attention only if it is sufficiently important for the self.

Attention is taken in charge by *the self.* What does this mean from the cerebral point of view? There is a constant succession of multiple images within us; but there is one image that is always present and to which we have learned to give a personal meaning. It is the image of self, whose formation in the parietal region we have discussed. Any process that is sufficiently intense to be *integrated into the image of self* will be conscious; any process that a barrier of relative *inhibition* leaves in the background will be unconscious.

Cerebral functioning should not be judged as if it were made up of independent processes. They are related. Among these processes, the gnosia of the image of self possesses a more *personalizing* role because it occurs in a more complex brain. It would be a mistake to deny the existence of a kind of consciousness in higher animals which certainly plays an active part in directing their behavior, but it would be another mistake to identify their consciousness with ours, which even from the cerebral point of view seems to be of a quite different order. This superiority is connected basically with the complexity of the brain, and man possesses it as an innate aptitude that does not depend on the maturation of his brain. But this complexity of the brain makes possible, here again, a verbalization, that of the image of self as well as of other images. One passes thus from an obscure reflexive ability to true reflection when the image of the body is replaced by "I" used as the subject of a sentence.

The structures of the sensory-motor brain of verbalized thought, above the regulatory apparatus and under its influence, are thus seen to be responsible for consciousness of self and the possibility of awareness, imagination, and will. A cerebral cogwheel, by its very nature, has a part in directing the brain. This consciousness of self situates us in space and time. A psychophysiology of the will is being developed as the result of the study of certain apraxias in which it is the *motor initiative* that is lost. Will resides in the structuration, through the consciousness, of the motor zones. In certain cases of poisoning, Baruk has observed animals which, although not paralyzed, are incapable of moving at will and remain in any position they are placed in, however strange it may be. The same thing is observed in *human catatonia.*

However, this second level of cerebral consciousness is not the highest. We have seen that our brain has two circuits for systems of conduct. On the one hand, there is the primitive brain of the rhinencephalon, which is responsible for instinctive and affective manifestations – calm and agitation, alimentary and sexual kinds of behavior, manifestations of pleasure, pain, anger. On the other hand, there is the brain of verbalized thought and awareness, the sensory-motor zone that may be called the *noetic brain* * of knowledge and action. Consciousness is not only verbalized thought, sensations, and will to act. It is the reflective search for a suitable conduct with a certain aim in view. Both the thinking machine of the noetic brain and the behavior machine of the primitive brain are therefore dependent upon it. This unification, which ensures personalizing integration and gives to individual consciousness its complete dimension, is achieved by the structures of the *prefrontal brain.*

Human development of the prefrontal zone (the fore-

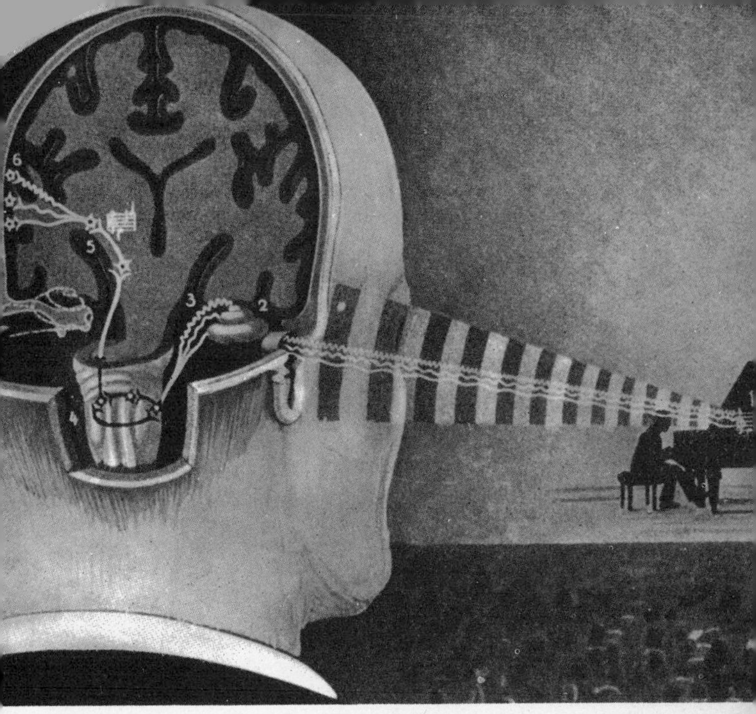

No music without a brain. No consciousness without a brain.

head) had raised the question whether this was the zone of intelligence. All past observations in pathology as well as animal experimentation and the examination of patients deprived of this region by lobotomy operations which had been justified by earlier results, have established that the prefrontal zone is the brain of self-control, well-balanced disposition, and reasonable worry and uneasiness in the face of one's duty. In pathological cases, this uneasiness changes into abnormal anxiety, which a disabling operation transforms into infantile indifference. It is the brain of the sense of what is coming, the sense of oneself and of others, and the sense of what is human; and it is because of it that social intercourse is not merely verbal dialogue but profound human relationship. In a word, this brain gives to the human personality its full dimension. It is not a rationalistic machine without *feelings,* * or an affective machine without logic and without *reason,* * but the union of what is rational and what is affective at a higher level which can be called *heart* and *love,* * assigning to these words their highest meaning. Human cerebral neurophysiology helps us to get away from the ambiguity of sentimentality and affectivity. There is an inferior sentimentality, such as that exploited by sensational newspapers, which depends on the primitive brain, and there is a superior sentimentality which goes beyond reason without being contrary to it and gives it its true human value. It depends on the prefrontal region. This zone of the brain is the organ of true freedom, which consists not only of mastery and choice among determinisms, but also of the search for a truly human kind of conduct, the only kind that preserves equilibrium and enables us to keep our freedom.

Indeed, a gratuitous kind of freedom to do just anything does not exist in man. He must discover what conforms to the development of his nature, under penalty of becoming dehumanized. The great difference between the animal brain and the human brain is that the animal has a rich innate supply of instincts that establish for him his normal conduct – instincts that depend chiefly on the hypothalamus. It has relatively little to learn. On the contrary, in man the hypothalamus is smaller and no longer commands truly instinctive kinds of behavior, but simple physiological processes. In man, everything is taken care of on the level of his habits, of conditioned reflexes. A rat whose adrenal gland has been removed knows enough to choose the salt water that will prevent it from dying, solely because of the sensitivity of its hypothalamus to the disequilibrium of its inner environment. Man has lost this instinct and creates gastronomy in order to be able to eat when not hungry. The animal has a sexual instinct that imposes upon it, in an innate way, the most complex kinds of behavior during courtship. In man, though a sexual need exists, the conditions of its exercise – even the notion of a partner of the opposite sex – are entirely acquired. Man is no longer the prey of instinct but becomes the slave of social customs which, grafted onto needs, have replaced instincts. He can therefore be free only by reflection, which, taking into account his real needs and his nature, will make him invent satisfactory kinds of behavior. This will be the role of the prefrontal functions.

The seriousness of a mutilation of this region can therefore be appreciated. It can only be considered the lesser of two evils, and several reports by patients who have undergone this operation have shown the suffering they experienced because of their loss. Fortunately, operations today are more and more selective and less and less mutilating. Above all, recourse to chemical sedatives limits the cases where psychosurgery * is called for and makes it possible to substitute for it a much more humane psychotherapy. *

Neurophysiology thus enables us to define a *norm,* * a *normal* human brain, functioning well, in perfectly integrated *equilibrium,* * with its three parts arranged in a perfect hierarchy.

The disturbances of cerebral integration

However, such a brain remains an ideal that is rarely realized. Whereas an animal is only slightly capable of progress, man owes to his brain an exceptional malleability, both as regards the individual and as regards the history of humanity, in which civilization is seen to be *man's art of using his brain better and better.*

Like the animal brain, the human brain is subject to all the anatomical and physiological deficiencies connected with its nature as a living organ. Its functioning will be more upset by lesions or disturbances in the inner environment because it is more complex. But there is a pathology peculiar to the human brain (or which at least assumes such proportions only in man) – namely, *mental pathology,* depending on disequilibriums caused directly by the poor functioning of an anatomically healthy brain. In addition to being the most complex organ, the human brain is the most fragile, the most easily tired, the one that most easily loses its equilibrium, in its adult state and especially during its formation.

Cerebral pathology may be viewed under three separate aspects. First, there are clearly localized lesions of a neurological order, which do not upset the psychism or consciousness but merely sensorial receptions or motor acts, the gnosias or the praxias. By contrast, there are *mental disturbances,* the object of *psychiatry* * – true illnesses of the mind in which consciousness is clouded or seriously disturbed. These *psychoses* * are often without anatomical lesions; this does not mean that the brain is normal, but its over-all functioning lacks equilibrium, as is demonstrated by the beneficent action that certain equilibrium-restoring shocks *(electric shock* *) can produce. The cause of these psychoses is not well understood, but the progress made in the field of the chemistry of the brain seems to be very promising in this respect. Between localized neurological disturbances and the generalized mental disturbances of the psychoses, there is finally a whole category of cerebral disequilibriums in which the purely physiological disturbance is connected with a kind of *partial disintegration* of cerebral functioning. These are the *neuroses,* of which *hysteria* * is the one known for the longest time. Neuroses have been carefully studied from the psychological point of view by *psychoanalysis,* * which has insisted on the role of *unconscious* * complexes, often repressed as a result of emotional shock in childhood *(repression* *), which are manifested either through psychic disequilibrium or through a *psychosomatic* * internal disorder.

Continuing the work of Pavlov *(Pavlovism* *), neurophysiology is beginning to determine precisely the cerebral phenomena that are responsible for neuroses. Pavlov was able to create neuroses in animals when there was a conflict between excitation and inhibition, which throws the whole brain off balance. For example, a dog trained to salivate at the sight of an ellipse and not at the sight of a circle has nervous attacks when the two figures are shown to him too close together. He no longer finds it possible to keep his equilibrium. The same is true of a cat that is trained to expect a good meal at a certain signal and that abruptly falls into a trap. It is understood that the repressions known to psychoanalysis are inhibitive conditioned reflexes which automatically prevent an awareness of a part of cerebral functioning. It is this disintegration, creating foci of activity in the unconscious, that is at the origin of neurotic kinds of behavior which are beyond the patient's control and of which he does not know the true motivation. These unconscious foci are particularly apt to be switched toward the primitive brain and the hypothalamus, and thus to disturb visceral activity in general. The awareness made possible by raising the inhibitive barrier through slow psychoanalysis (or, quickly, through *narcoanalysis* *) can suppress the disturbance by re-establishing cerebral integration.

Alongside these psychosomatic disturbances, in which the basal centers are in a state of disequilibrium that begins in the brain itself, must be placed the pseudo-neuroses of nervous *fatigue*, * in which the fatigue of the regulatory basal centers causes both visceral disturbances and cerebral disequilibriums.

Education on the one hand and living conditions on the other ought to be such as to favor cerebral equilibrium. But that is not enough. It is possible for a man with a normal brain not to be made unbalanced, but to make himself unbalanced if he does not use his brain correctly – that is, in an integrated and orderly way. Letting one's instincts run wild or burying oneself in conformity are practices that are as unbalancing as neurotic repressions. It is not a matter of a mind acting upon a brain which acts upon the rest of the body; rather there is a brain, an organ of the body and subject to its influence, whose functioning assures the psychism and in turn affects most decisively the entire organic functioning.

We have pointed out that modern electronic machines offer us complex electrical circuits that are not unlike cerebral circuits. *Cybernetics* has enabled us to understand the functional relations between psychism and the brain. Neurophysiologists have profited from the construction of behavior machines, such as the electronic turtles of Grey Walter, because these models help us to understand certain cerebral mechanisms such as conditioned reflexes.

Must we conclude from this that the only difference between the brain and a machine lies in the fact that machines are still a long way from cerebral complexity? The neurophysiologist cannot admit such a conclusion. He is interested by the comparison of machines and the brain, but what he expects from it above all is a better distinction between the possibilities of what is mechanical and what

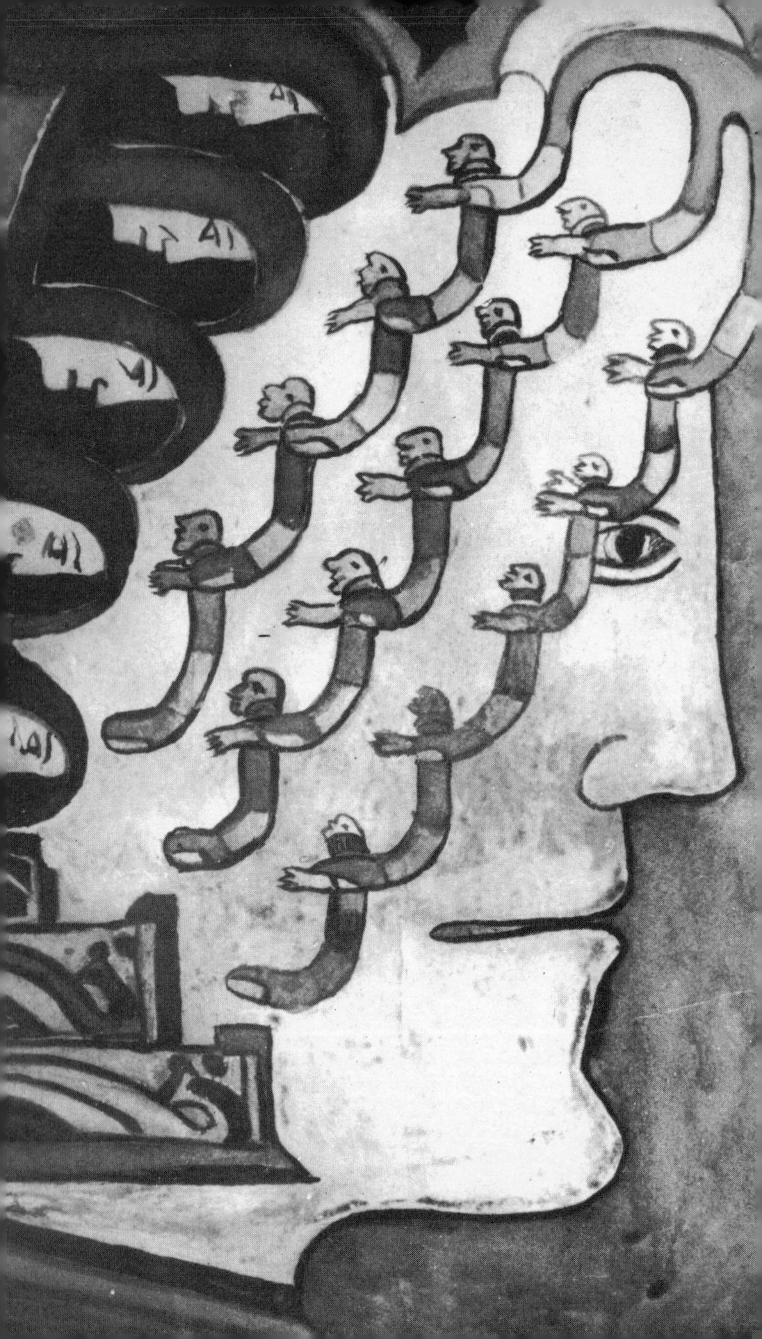

is human – that is, what is alive.

The principal difference is to be found in connection with processes of integration and of consciousness. The machine is made up of inert cogwheels connected from the outside by an engineer. Even if it were built by another machine, that would still be an outside impetus made possible by an inventor's ingenuity. Machines do not think by themselves; they are only perfected tools at the service of human thought. On the contrary, the brain, made up of living cells, has constructed itself in the course of embryonic development by virtue of the biological characteristics of the organism. Each cogwheel is a small world by itself, a cell endowed with a sensitivity, a kind of behavior, and an elementary interiority; these, though far from our cerebral consciousness, are nonetheless analogues of it. They are what may be called a *bioconsciousness.* * We are closer to an amoeba, with its integrated inferior psychism, than to a robot. The superior organism, such as man's, made up of innumerable cells, finds its unity in its integration. Like cellular integration, organic integration has a psychological aspect which culminates in cerebral integration, the source of true consciousness, which thus is seen to be a child of life, destined to be forever lacking in the robot, however self-regulated it may be.

Drawing by a madman.

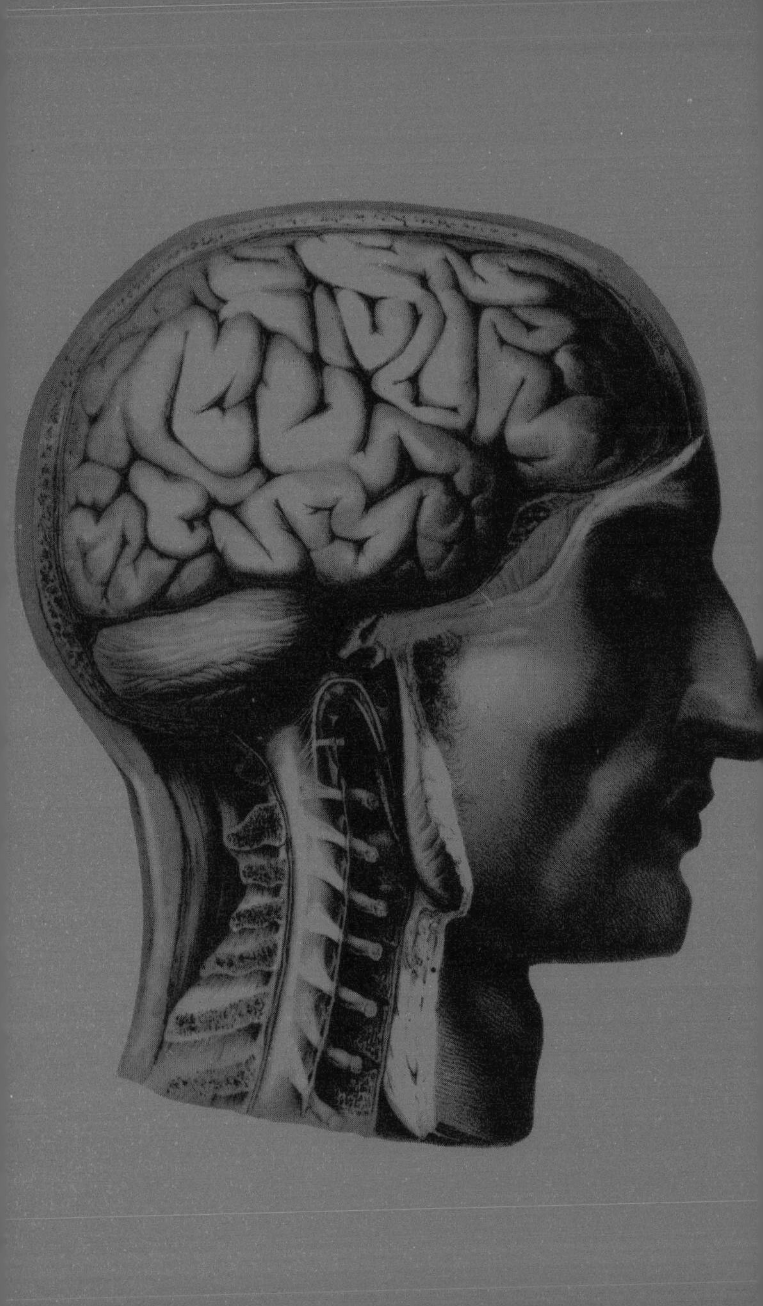

Man the Master of his Brain

Know thyself

We are a long way from knowing as much about the cerebral organ as we know about our other organs. Nevertheless, our knowledge of it has made considerable progress and places at our disposal important possibilities of action. We are no longer completely helpless in the face of cerebral disturbances, even psychoses. The atmosphere of asylums is in the process of being thoroughly transformed; instead of being inhuman hells that complete the destruction of the insane, they are becoming places of peace where people often recover mental *health.* * We owe all this to progress in our knowledge of the physiology of the brain.

People understand more and more that the brain is not just another organ whose functioning may arouse curiosity or interest the specialist. It is not an ordinary mechanism; it is the organ that makes of man a man, a person. Organ of thought and action, it presides over the highest psychic functions while at the same time acting on the functioning organism in general through the nervous system. It is therefore the organ of health, of life that is balanced and fully human. Because of this psychosomatic unity of which it is the agent, any somatic disturbance has a repercussion on the brain and tends to cause a mental disturbance; any mental worry becomes a factor in organic illness. *Everything acts upon the brain and the brain acts upon everything.* There is no therapy in which the brain and the nervous system are not involved. This point of view, which derives from modern neurophysiology, is not yet sufficiently widespread. Scientific medicine still remains a medical science of organs which forgets the whole – that is, man. Psychosomatic medicine is often treated as a new specialty. There are those who, claiming to defend human spiritual values, affirm their total transcendence, and so the modern scientific and technical community, which is oriented in the direction of the quantitative analysis of material phenomena, loses all interest in them; but the powers of this community are such that there is a risk of bringing mankind to its downfall. The true defense of what is spiritual ought to be realistic and based on the manner in which this spiritual quality takes form in man thanks to the functioning of the brain.

Under these conditions, there is no human activity that does not need to take account of this brain upon which it is based. The scientific and technical world must be given knowledge of the organ of science and technique so that it will learn to respect it and to use it correctly. It is incredible that popularizations should tell us more and more about machines and yet we should know ourselves so badly. It is outrageous that we should respect machines and neglect to respect man and the care of his health. Progress ought to be at the service of man, whereas in reality it is often dehumanizing because engineers, technicians, and the men in charge are inexcusably ignorant of human biology and persist in separating what belongs to the body from what belongs to the mind and spirit.

More and more the development of a *scientific culture* is called for. This will be useful and complete only if this culture, like traditional culture, achieves a humanistic synthesis. As a matter of fact, knowledge of the brain is a scientific knowledge of man as man which does not in the least invalidate, but rather confirms, traditional values by giving them an objective basis.

Whoever we may be, we are responsible for our health and for that of others. The problems of *mental hygiene* are immense and involve the whole organization of society; they are problems that belong to politics. But these problems will be solved only if everyone becomes aware of them, only if we are no longer involuntary and unconscious guinea pigs shaped by equally involuntary and unconscious sorcerers' apprentices, with everyone being equally ignorant, and ignorant in a way that has become inexcusable. *Brain hygiene* concerns our daily way of life and its influence on those around us; as long as we have not learned how to live, it will be useless to hope for great general reforms. It is not the government or the police that should impose a hygiene unaccompanied by understanding; it is up to everyone to understand such things as, for example, the necessity of fighting against noise, which is a brain poison, or against toxic fumes.

We are much too much inclined to wait passively for the harmony of equilibrium and health to come to us, to expect it to result from outside conditions that require no personal effort on our part. Although there are extreme cases, particularly in mental pathology, in which the patient can have his equilibrium restored without his knowledge, as it were, just as a machine is repaired, it must be affirmed that most of the time we can be cured only with our collaboration; the doctor helps us to cure ourselves, to recover control. Drugs, in particular, should not be counterposed to psychotherapy; they are a means of creating favorable conditions for psychotherapy, artificial aids that enable us to get hold of ourselves more easily.

Since we all possess this extraordinary human brain which makes possible all our human spiritual qualities, we ought to know it well enough to avoid misusing it, but rather use it to the fullest. The various specialists in the human sciences can make their disciplines fully efficacious in the service of man only by abandoning relativism. They must base their efforts instead on the common denominator of research aimed at better cerebral functioning. A kind of council of specialists who, in varying degrees, are concerned with our brain – medical doctors as well as psychologists and sociologists – ought to be available to teach us what is good for us and to help us to achieve it freely.

Constituted as the organ of psychosomatic unity, our brain is simutaneously responsible for phenomena of very different types. All the somatic motor commands are cerebral structures, but so also is thought, in terms of images as well as verbalized thought. Social relationships, too, are cerebral structures. Our brain gives us the image of the other person with his name; it makes dialogue possible and conditions the obscure social need at the level of the basal centers, just as it generates the real awareness of the other person, of his rights and duties in regard to us and of ours in regard to him at the level of the prefrontal structures, which constitute the organ of love – that is, of individual and social integration. Everything that acts upon man, not only physiological factors but also psychological and social factors, can therefore be expressed in cerebral neurophysiological terms of equilibrium and disequilibrium. Everything involves the brain. To state the laws of mental equilibrium precisely is to give an objective basis for all human conduct. It is possible, through a parallel effort, either to determine which are the most human forms of behavior in the light of neurophysiological laws, or to see whether a contested moral precept is in accord with the laws of human cerebral equilibrium.

Inversely, it is possible to consider everything which deprives the brain of equilibrium objectively bad. A great deal of advice on how to behave correctly would be more precise and efficacious if its neurophysiological aspect were developed more fully. Means of regaining complementary equilibrium can be found in all the areas controlled by the brain. There is not merely a unique medical therapy treating the brain as just another organ, as for instance in surgical therapy and use of shock or drugs. All psychotherapy, whether it involves one person, two, or a group, is also a reshaping of the brain thanks to language signals – whether internal language or dialogue, social relationships, or re-education through work. Materal as well as mental kinds of therapy act through the brain. To these must be added all the more or less intermediate psychophysical kinds of therapy, such as narcoanalysis (in which psychotherapy acts upon a brain which the drug has made more malleable), methods of conditioning and unconditioning, of *relaxation,* * and of physical exercise (which is always psychophysical). If sick persons can be cured by methods of various kinds (which work even better when used together), it is also possible to use many of these methods to preserve one's health and personal equilibrium.

Doctors and surgeons of the brain

The conditions of the modern world, which are often unfavorable to cerebral equilibrium, and our ignorance, which makes us take dangerous chances, sometimes result in making our brain sick. We then have recourse to the doctor, the neuropsychiatrist. Because of the progress made in all techniques and all neurophysiological knowledge, the neuropsychiatrist has become capable of treating the brain effectively by various means. It is no longer a question of sorcerers' apprentices and involuntary guinea pigs, but of voluntary guinea pigs and specialists who work together consciously to restore the brain to equilibrium. Although our knowledge is still very incomplete, progress in the medical science of the brain has been considerable during recent years. It is true to say that today we possess great possibilities of preventing and curing numerous cerebral disturbances. This progress in medical knowledge would be still more useful if the doctor took into consideration the full significance of the organ he is repairing, and if he knew how to approach the human problems in the patient's life. In the absence of these concerns, therapy will remain inadequate. It is impossible to treat and cure a brain without being concerned about the conditions under which it is used – the patient's environment and his habits.

Obviously, there is cause for rejoicing in the progress of therapy, especially when one sees patients cured who would formerly have been considered hopeless, or when new kinds of therapy make possible greater efficiency with less danger, as is the case today when we see the brutal methods of shock and psychosurgery recede in importance to be replaced by psychotherapy and *ergotherapy* * applied to patients who have been calmed by new chemical tranquilizers. * But this improved knowledge of the causes of disequilibrium, which increasingly enables us to treat them, goes hand in hand with living conditions that are contrary to cerebral hygiene and that increase the causes of disequilibrium, and so we lose in one way what we gain in another. Cerebral overwork becomes the cause of numerous neuroses and of psychosomatic disturbances that are pathogenic in themselves and that create a predisposition to all illnesses, aggravate them, and make them more difficult to cure. How can a sick liver, stomach, or ovary be brought back to its normal state when it is constantly subjected to disturbances of nervous origin? How can a case of tuberculosis be cured when the patient's condition is poor because of his personal problems, which in many cases have played a very important role in the onset of his sickness by reducing his resistance?

It must never be forgotten that being able to treat the brain of a sick man means also being able to influence the brain of a man who is well. The moral limitations which are the only barrier preventing the exploitation of these immense possibilities of human manipulation are generally accepted but may not be regarded as binding by a political totalitarianism in search of efficient controls.

People are justifiably preoccupied with the repercussions on man of modern civilization and, first of all, with the dangers of the increase of radioactivity in nature, which will necessarily make the earth uninhabitable for man. Except for certain specialists such as, for example, Jean Rostand, much less thought is given to the frightening powers that biology today gives us over man. They are ambiguous powers, capable of being used for good as well as for evil, and all the more ambiguous because it is not always even possible to define what is good and what is evil. No fully realized human nature exists. Man does not live by fixed instincts; his ways of life change in the course of history and science can modify them. Man is very malleable, but not all manipulations are healthy ones. We must always be concerned with the difficult search for what helps to make our nature develop and flourish, and with rejecting what is unnatural. It is possible to work toward perfecting man – that is, to help him to be more himself – but it is also possible, using the building of a new man as a pretext, to dehumanize him completely.

The responsibility of biologists today is therefore great, especially in two fields. The first is that of genetics, of heredity, of all the modifications to which human sexuality can be subjected now and in the future. The second concerns our subject: it involves cerebral shaping. In this case it is no longer the body of man or his species that we treat,

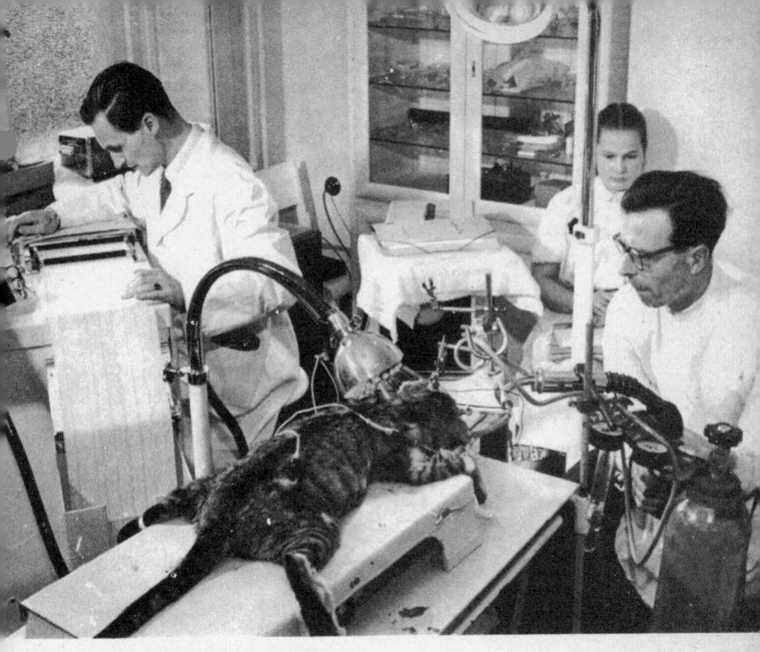

Action of narcosis on a cat recorded with the help of an electroencephalogram.

but the mind and the spirit, the soul. Today, if we wanted to, we could modify anybody's personality and place neurophysiology at the service of mental derangement. What we have said about the prefrontal functions shows us that lobotomy operations diminish the personality by bringing about the loss of human uneasiness and worry about the future, create indifference to cherished opinions, increase accessibility to *suggestion.* * Certain drugs, the hypnotics of narcoanalysis or tranquilizers taken in overdoses, have analogous effects. The more progress we make in the secrets of the chemistry of the brain and the more success we have in restoring the equilibrium of the insane, the more dangerous means will we have at our disposal for modifying behavior to suit our desires. With certain *hallucinatory drugs* * that have long been used by some artists but that have been improved recently, one can create real states of temporary artificial madness. What a temptation for a totalitarian regime to overcome the resistance of opponents by such methods and to have perfectly docile, obedient, and conforming subjects! For that matter, such violent methods are not really necessary. A whole set of procedures based upon the conditioned reflexes in a weakened brain, with rewards or punishments, makes it possible today to shape the personality (this is what is called, in newspaper terminology, *"brainwashing"* *). Whether successful or not, the procedure is, in any shape or form, inhuman and dangerous to the internal equilibrium. All the progress made by the psychological and the social sciences, by revealing to us the secret of human motivations, enables us to orient the brain at will toward a particular kind of behavior. Do you want people to be rebellious or docile? Either type can be produced at will, under the most completely relativistic outlook, without any concern for understanding the human personal context of this docility or of this rebelliousness, whether it is favorable to cerebral functioning and therefore to the individual's true development, and whether its tendency is neurotic or liberating.

These moral considerations had to be mentioned. They are not irrelevant to neurophysiology, since this science confirms the moral norm with cerebral equilibrium as a basis. Let us now review the various aspects of medical treatment of the brain. All we shall be doing, in this connection, is observing from the therapeutic point of view what we have previously pointed out from the physiological viewpoint.

Exploration of the brain

Our knowledge of what is going on in any particular part of the brain is increasing daily. We need merely remind ourselves of what has been accomplished in the field of electrical exploration by external electroencephalography or internal electrocorticography, the latter aided in precision by stereotactic apparatuses. But there are other methods, less useful from the physiological point of view, of looking into the brain. There are, for example, all the *radiographic** methods. Ordinary radiography can reveal the opacity of a tumor, the transparency of a cyst. But certain procedures

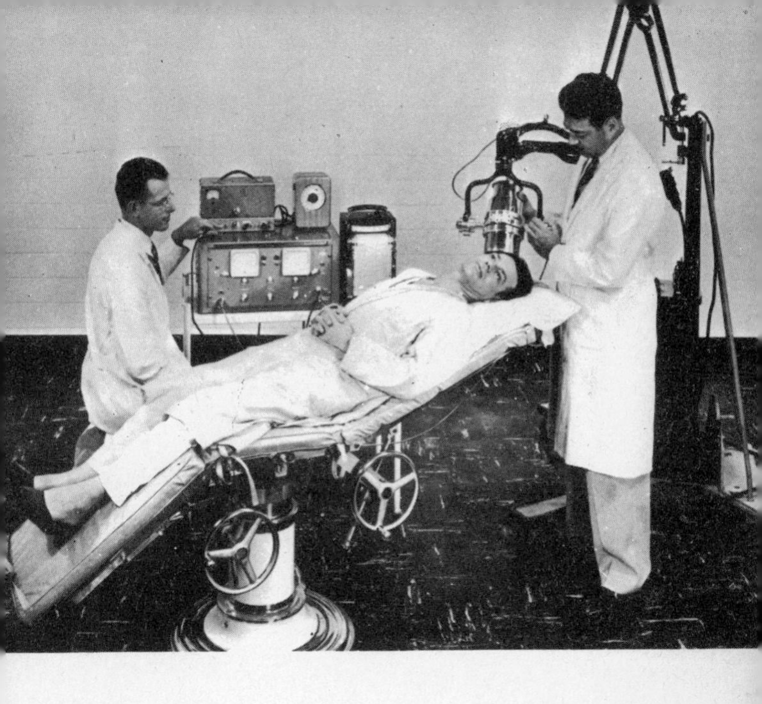

can be employed to facilitate radiographic analysis. By injecting air, or a substance that remains opaque to X rays, into the cerebral ventricles it is possible to see these ventricles and locate in relation to them a pathological formation which may restrict or compress them. An opaque substance with an iodine base can be injected into the arteries of the brain. This kind of *angiography* * makes it still easier to locate a diseased region. More recently, recourse has been had to the injection of radioactive substances containing trace elements that have an affinity for pathological formations, tumors. They can be located by exploration with a Geiger counter. Naturally, in addition to direct exploration of the brain, all the neurological somatic signs of cerebral disturbances or all psychological signs will always be very valuable for therapeutic indications. It is for this reason that massive lobotomies are less and less frequently performed today. In order to adapt

Radiography of the brain.

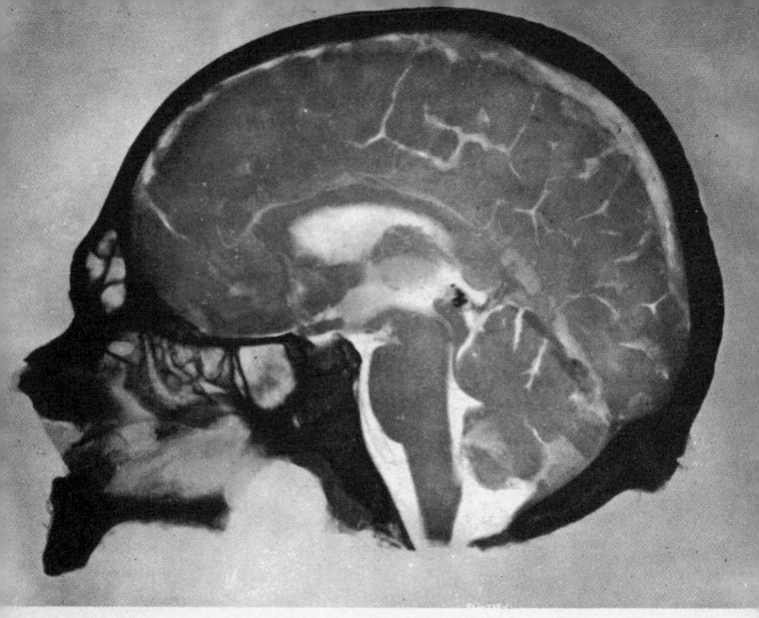

The brain: radiographic montage (photo by Delmas and Pertuset).

the prefrontal operation to the type of disturbance and perform what Lebeau calls *selective frontal surgery*, the patient must be subjected to very careful tests before the operation. The tests are resumed afterward to see whether the operation has been successful.

Electrical exploration of the brain is made when it is in repose, or else during spontaneous or stimulated activity, during sensorial excitations, or while it is in a state of gaseous alkalosis caused by hyperpnea.

When, by means of preparatory examinations that sometimes include actual small-scale operations with minor *trepanation*, * a diagnosis of remediable cerebral lesion has been established, medical science has various procedures at its disposal. These are, essentially, destruction, section, and ablation (procedures involving surgery or radiotherapy); next, methods of shock; and finally, therapeutic medicaments. Let us point out that certain physical agents, such as electricity, ionization, and heat, are also very efficacious in either a direct or reflex way *(reflexotherapy *)*. A number of therapeutic possibilities for the future are to be found here.

Brain surgery

Brain surgery, which is a very special and very precise form of modern surgery, created by such pioneers as Harvey Cushing and, in France, De Martel and Clovis Vincent, requires special techniques. First of all, in order to lay the brain bare, recourse is had to trepans provided with automatic release mechanisms to prevent injury to the organ. Although anesthesia – often local – is required for noncerebral tissues, the cerebral operation itself, as we have already mentioned, is performed upon the wide-awake subject, since the brain is insensitive to pain; in this way it is possible to keep closer track of the patient's condition. The operation is delicate because it is necessary to avoid injuring the healthy parts, to avoid hemorrhages, and above all to operate very gently so that irritation will not lead to grave complications in the form of cerebral swelling by *edema,* * which impedes the nutrition of the brain. Surgery does not always have to enter the brain when all that is involved is an external compression. One can use preparatory excitations to be sure of just where one is. Instead of destroying surgically, one can make a local electrocoagulation or inject a local anesthetic such as cocaine, which will have a calming effect. The destructive effect of ultra-high-frequency sound waves can also be used. In certain lobotomy operations, all one does is move the eye aside, pass through the roof of the socket, and introduce a cutting instrument which, moving blindly in a semicircle, severs the bundles of white matter of the prefrontal region.

The surgeon is concerned with the brain from a threefold point of view. First of all, there is *neurological* surgery intended to remove tumors or pathological growths that press upon the nervous system, or to treat certain diseased centers, such as the corpus striatum, which is responsible for shaking in Parkinson's disease. This kind of surgery

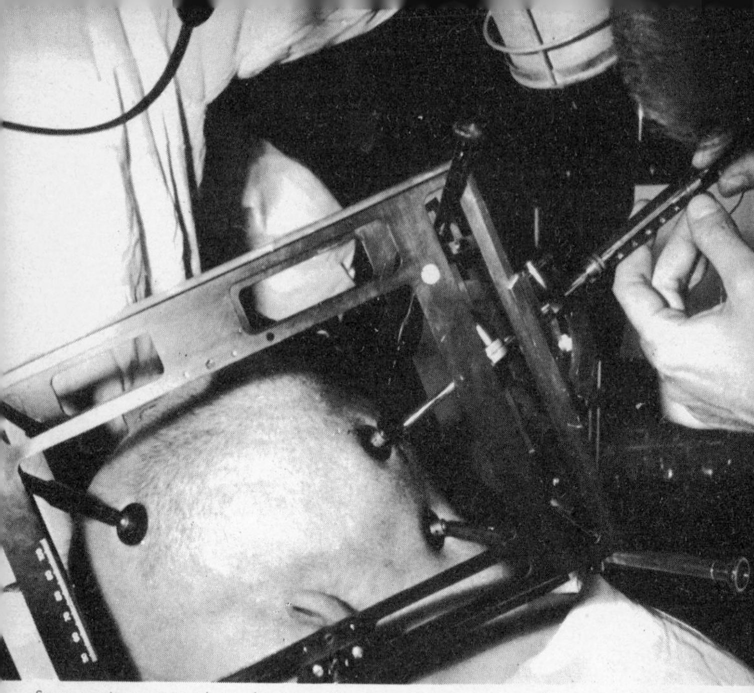

Stereotactic apparatus that makes it possible to reach a precise point of the brain and to proceed with electroagulation.

is not directly concerned with the psychism. It is a branch of neurology, the theoretical and medical science of localized lesions of the brain which cause motor and sensory disturbances rather than mental disturbances.

Then, in connection with psychiatry (the science of mental disorders which are also cerebral disturbances, though disturbances of purely physiological cerebral integration, often without localized lesions), there has been developed a *psychosurgery* – physiological surgery intended to restore equilibrium to the psychism itself by making sections in the brain. It was born in 1936 when the Portuguese psychiatrist Egas Moniz dared to transpose to man the results of Fulton's physiological analysis based on animals, by performing the first prefrontal lobotomies.

Psychosurgery underwent a great deal of development after 1945. It is losing ground somewhat. There are two

Neurosurgical operation.

basic types of operation: severing the white matter, which disconnects the diseased prefrontal lobe and prevents it from acting *(leukotomy);* and performing an ablation of the gray matter of this region *(topectomy *).* It involves, therefore, a cerebral mutilation, a lesser evil which, before the use of tranquilizers, could be regarded as a benefit. Very violent discussions have been held over the lawfulness of this operation, which a Pavlovian respect for the brain has caused to be forbidden in the USSR. The reports of some patients who are aware of how much they have lost by the operation are heartrending; on the other hand, other cases are more favorable. Cures are effected – with no assurance of success – only by multilating an

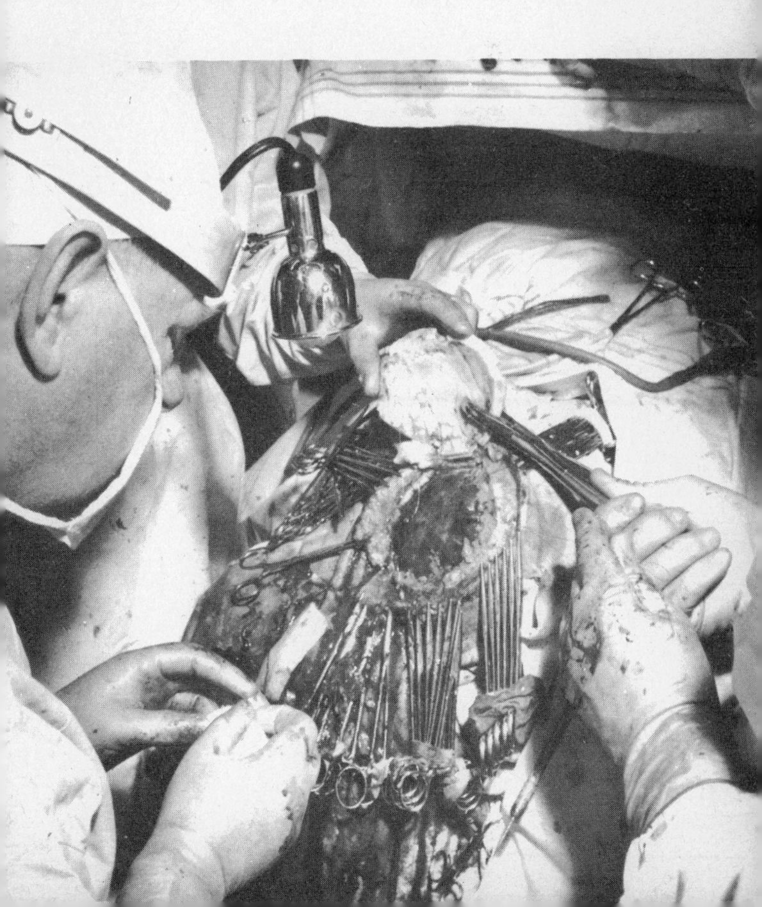

essential part of the brain, frequently turning the patient into a kind of overgrown, impulsive, and indifferent child. There have been abuses; but even so, other psychiatrists, following Baruk's example, have gone rather far in their condemnation, out of a legitimate respect for the personality. These operations are aimed chiefly at disturbances of the disposition (melancholia or manic depression), and also cases of great grief the causes of which cannot be done away with and which the lobotomy does not prevent but makes psychologically bearable by removing the anguish connected with them. Today they are becoming more restricted because we have learned to recognize which regions should be destroyed depending on the various cases. It is not only the inner or outer prefrontal region that is operated on, but also the various parts of the rhinencephalon or certain basal nuclei. But it is the development of chemical sedatives that increasingly reduces the reasons for these serious operations. (Let us point out that if the lobotomy is to be effective, it should always be bilateral.)

In addition to neurosurgeons, all surgeons and particularly specialists in cardiac surgery should also be concerned about the brain. As the organ with the most urgent need for blood, oxygen, and food, it is the first to suffer from disturbances in the external environment. After circulation has stopped for one minute, there is no longer any electrical activity; after several minutes, irreparable lesions are produced. As soon as a respiratory or circulatory syncope occurs, one must accordingly take care to avoid cerebral lesions, and the object of the various procedures used for *reanimation* * is first of all to save the brain. That is why it was necessary to wait before interrupting circulation in cardiac surgery until there were artificial pumps powerful enough to irrigate the brain. Even today, it is this factor that limits the length of operations. By lowering the internal temperature after blocking *thermoregulation,* * it is true that one plunges the brain into a coma, but its requirements are considerably diminished and it does not suffer. *Hibernation,* * accordingly, makes it possible to delay reanimation. Fear of cardiac fibrillation has prevented going much below 30 degrees C. in the case of human beings thus far, but with rats and monkeys it has been possible to lower the internal temperature to 0 degrees C. and to achieve a truly *latent life* * in which the heart and breathing stop without any damage to the cells, whose requirements are reduced. By warming up first of all the respiratory center and the heart, one sets the organism into normal motion again; even conditioned reflexes acquired though training have not been destroyed. It is possible that this technique may provide us in the future with a means of super-rest and cerebral disintoxication. It sometimes happens that the brain is no longer capable of coming back to life and that all efforts to reanimate it are doomed to failure. We now possess the means that will enable us to diagnose this "death of the brain."

Cerebral shock and sleep cure

Psychosurgery is not the only violent method capable of restoring a certain psychic harmony. It had been noticed earlier, clinically and quite empirically, that certain kinds of *shock therapy* had an analogous effect. Among these are the drop in blood sugar brought about by *insulin,* * the injection of a convulsant such as *metrazol,* and causing an epileptic fit by a short and violent electrical excitation of the brain *(electric shock).* These actions involve both a loss of consciousness with coma (due to a cerebral inhibition connected with the activity of the basal regulatory apparatus) and convulsive crises resulting from the excitation of lower centers. This shock therapy is a destructuration of the pathological brain which, when it regains consciousness, sometimes recovers normal structures. Here again, the abuses that have been committed should not make us forget the importance of such methods before the era of tranquilizers.

In other psychiatric cases – especially neuroses, psychosomatic disturbances, and disturbances caused by nervous fatigue – restoration of the brain is achieved by sleep cures. This use of the normal means of rest for the brain is all the more beneficial if the subjects are victims of insomnia as the result of an abnormal excitation of the regulatory apparatus. Efforts are made to create as normal a sleep as possible by gradually decreasing the hypnotic dose through the use (without the patient's knowledge) of place-

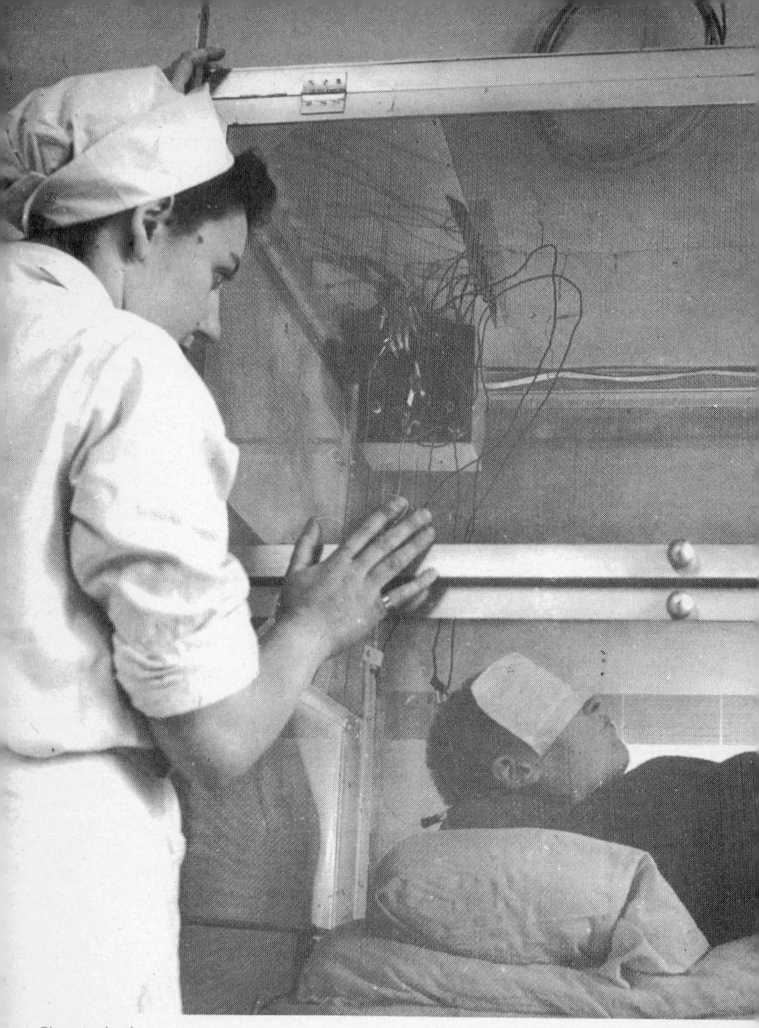

Electric shock.

bos (conditioned reflex sleep). At the same time one tries to create the kind of atmosphere that is most favorable to sleep. Although it has quite different principles and goals, hibernation is also a comatherapy.

Brain medicaments

Man has always found some substances, mostly in vegetable form, that he could absorb and let act upon his psychism in order to achieve sleep or stimulation, to kill pain, etc. All civilizations have managed to discover artificial paradises. Certain plants made it possible to bring about delirium or hallucinations used in religious observances. Note, for example, the role of Indian hemp or hashish in the Orient, that of the coca leaf in the Andes, or that of the opium poppy. Everywhere and at all times, men have prepared alcohol. Modern chemistry, in the last hundred years, has been able to isolate the elements responsible for these actions and to prepare innumerable artificial substances capable of acting upon the nervous system. The old opium poppy has accordingly yielded its place to morphine, the coca leaf to cocaine. It is amazing to realize that something as common today as aspirin was born with this century.

All the medicaments of the nervous system are poisons which, taken in larger doses, are dangerous; they are therefore toxic substances that must be employed with certain precautions – the most dangerous ones must be used under medical supervision. In any case, it is always important to be cautious. There is always a certain amount of poisoning, however small, and often a developing tolerance that makes it necessary to increase the doses in order to preserve the effect. Sometimes a state of real need is created, when the neurons have grown used to the drug and find themselves in a state of serious disequilibrium in its absence; this is what accounts for accidents during withdrawal. The phenomenon is manifested at its fullest in the great *toxicomanias* * such as morphinomania, cocainomania, and alcoholism, which make people sick. The only way they can be cured is by medical disintoxication, which restores the nervous system while at the same time avoiding serious withdrawal disturbances.

Alongside these substances, a special place must be assigned to minor excitants such as coffee, small doses of alcohol, and tobacco, which are less dangerous when not used to excess. Certain agents that act upon the nervous system are less harmful because they are natural substances that are real food for the brain. In addition to oxygen, which in large doses is toxic, and glucose, let us mention more specific substances such as phosphoric acid, fats, certain vitamins, and glutamic acid. The last-named, which has been baptized *"intelligence pill"* * in newspaper language, has been responsible for improving the training of rats and the IQ of deficient children, but it is not at all capable of increasing intelligence or memory under normal conditions.

Among the many types of nerve drugs, we may distinguish excitants, sedatives, and substances with a more specific action. The *excitants* are fairly dangerous, for they make it possible, in complete euphoria, to go beyond one's forces. As agents of short-lived effort, they dope and do not provide a real remedy for the fatigued brain, which would consist of rest and not an increased artificial effort. Particularly dangerous and capable of causing real psychiatric disturbances are some of the *psychotonic amines,* or amphetamines, which students have wisely been forbidden to use and which made possible the doping of German soldiers in 1940.

The depressants, or sedatives, range from the brutal effect of the *general anesthetics,* such as ether, which causes a reversible toxic coma (or *narcosis,* used in surgery), to simple *hypnotics,* such as the barbiturates, which induce an almost normal sleep but which, if used habitually, are as dangerous for one's equilibrium as excitants. Other substances have a more specific action on certain basal nervous centers, such as pain relievers *(analgesics* *: aspirin, morphine, etc.) and those used to reduce fever. The past decade has seen the development of a whole group of substances called *neuroleptics* * or *tranquilizers* – sedatives which neither excite nor cause sleep but which put the irritated regulatory centers at rest. These are the drugs for nervous tension, emotivity, anxiety. It is they which have revolutionized the psychiatric asylum and have reduced the use of violent methods by making psychotherapy possible; and by blocking thermoregulation they have also permitted artificial hibernation. The outstanding one, studied first in France, particularly by Delay, is *chlorpromazine* (commercially known as "largactyl"); we should also mention *reserpine.* In addition, there are numerous less dangerous agents whose use is becoming more and more common. Abuses are beginning to be apparent, and it is not without uneasiness that psychologists are observing the development of this "happiness toxicomania" resulting from lack of interest, indifference, and refusal to accept responsibilities.

After pointing out the convulsive and anticonvulsive agents, we shall end this brief review by mentioning *stupefacients.* What they have in common, in spite of their great variety, is the fact that they are above all modifiers of the psychism, often producing hallucinations, a kind of dream state. Besides morphine, cocaine, and alcohol, the following substances produce these effects to the maximum: hashish, particularly marijuana, and above all peyotl, that Mexican cactus from which one obtains mescaline, which causes visual hallucinations and a curious displacement in time and space. More recently, derivatives of rye ergot have provided chemists with *lysergic acid amine,* a very active hallucinatory agent which has made possible the development of a kind of experimental psychiatry, while the sacred mushrooms of Mexico led Heim to *psilocybine,* the most recent of the modifiers of the psychism, which has just begun to be used medically. It is likely that, as we continue in this direction, progress in our knowledge will provide us with the elective chemical agents of psychoses, especially when we know the substances that seem to be responsible for them.

Psychological access to the brain

These physical and chemical means of modifying the state of the brain are only one of the ways of getting at this organ – the objective, material, organic way of standard medical science. Because of the brain's functions, there exists another way, the psychological and functional approach, which is more subjective and is intended to restore to the patient a correct manner of using his brain, particularly by restructuring it through language, dialogue, and certain procedures of psychophysiological education. It is much too widely believed that *psychotherapy* is a purely psychic therapy. Its psychic character, which gives it a thoroughly human interpersonal dimension, nonetheless depends on the modification of cerebral structures by the signals of language, and this is not so very different from the action of a shock or a drug. First of all, psychotherapy involves all the recommendations made by mental hygiene (especially a sympathetic interest in other people). There are elaborate forms of psychotherapy that require specialists. Two tendencies that often intermingle should be distinguished. Either we bring about, to a greater or lesser degree, a loss of consciousness in order to suppress distrust and impose a change of behavior by suggestion; or, on the contrary, we try to heighten consciousness, to make the subject become conscious of himself, to make him reflect, come to decisions, increase and re-direct his will power. These two methods, of which the second is more humane and more profitable, often show comparable reactions. Thus labor pains may disappear in the kind of anesthesia brought about by hypnotic sleep and suggestion, but may also disappear – and disappear much better – as the result of becoming aware of the art of using one's brain to give birth correctly, without suffering. This Pavlovian psychoprophylactic method provides us with a first and remarkable example of what we may expect from a science of personal conduct advised by the brain.

The prototype of sleep psychotherapies is *hypnosis,* which can be used more successfully with some subjects than with others; it consists of sleep caused by processes of inhibition that were explained by Pavlov, but it involves the maintenance of a connection with the hypnotizer, whose orders are obeyed even if they concern the future (posthypnotic suggestion). Hypnosis can be dangerous but it is very effective. Its possibilities are far from having been exhausted. One variant is *chemical hypnosis.* Everyone is hypnotizable in the state of half-sleep produced by hypnotics. As the saying "In vino veritas" has it, an alcoholic cannot keep a secret and can be influenced by suggestion. The medical application of this *narcoanalysis* has been useful in facilitating a rapid psychoanalysis by removing the inhibiting effects of repressions, thus making possible a restoration of cerebral equilibrium; as in the use of electric

Sleep. Hypnosis is no longer merely a way to amuse the public but is also used in the doctor's office.

shock therapy, the psychosomatic disturbances of neuroses are suppressed. It is not at all a "truth serum" and its use by judges or the police is both morally contestable and dangerous, for the subject can still lie and, above all, he can be influenced by suggestion.

Among the active methods (which also carry the risk of suggestion) must be listed the varieties of *psychoanalysis* – a means of restoring the equilibrium of neurotics by a slow exploration of the unconscious aimed at uncovering the emotional conflicts of childhood, the origins of disturbing inhibitions, of repressions, and of *sublimations.* * Let us mention the methods aiming at equilibrium-restoring *psychophysical* activity. There are numerous possibilities that are as yet little exploited scientifically and not well known. Many of the secrets of Hindu medicine and of *yoga* * are based upon a genuine intuitive knowledge of the conditions of cerebral equilibrium, and it would be worthwhile to study them scientifically. It has been proved that certain positions and certain breathing exercises are useful.

Let us note still more particularly *ergotherapy* (re-education by an appropriate kind of work) and the various methods of relaxation in which the muscular slackening of the nervous, tense patient results from the fact that the regulatory centers of the base of the brain are at rest; this cerebral relaxation is therefore obtained by mechanisms very much like those of hypnosis or sleep cures. At first a very physical, muscular method, relaxation is becoming more and more psychological and similar to hypnosis, particularly in Schultz's *autogenous training*. This almost psychoanalytic aspect of cerebral relaxation which has to do with the teacher's influence is today being developed. This is certainly a method of restoring personal equilibrium that has a promising future.

Exercises in physical training are actually, as we have seen, exercises in *cerebral training*, in the development of conditioned reflexes and praxias. They are intended to provide not merely muscle but also brain. The whole hygiene of physical education and of sports can therefore be a kind of cerebral education with humanistic implications. Let us also mention, among the innumerable possible ways in which environment can exert an influence, the use of music to help restore equilibrium.

In addition to the pure psychologist, it seems that the future belongs to the *reflexologist* – that is, to the man who will teach everyone the conditioned reflexes that contribute to equilibrium and control as well as to the suppression of dangerous reflexes. The "cerebral adviser" will teach people how to make use of the many still unexploited possibilities of healing our brain. Brainwashing, which we have mentioned, is a complex set of various procedures intended to change the personality by acting upon the brain; it is a variety of suggestion. What must be created is a real brainwashing that would aid equilibrium and freedom, based upon personal mastery and reflection, a development of our true possibilities, the exaltation and not the abasement of consciousness and freedom. The future of humanity surely depends on the way in which this cerebral manipulation is understood – on whether it is made into an anti-

individual depersonalization, as often happens today, or whether, on the contrary, it becomes a means of superpersonalization. In the former case, we shall move toward an abnormal totalitarianism; in the latter, it will be possible to follow the paths leading toward an enrichment of what is personal by means of what is social – that *noosphere* * which Teilhard de Chardin suggests we work toward. It is up to us to set this as our goal.

Equilibrium through music.

Neurophysiology and morality

When, as a neurophysiologist, one reflects on human problems, one sees that they can all be approached from a cerebral point of view, since the brain is the organ of all human life and particularly of intellectual and psychic life. Now, what do we see all around us if not people who, whether voluntarily or not and whether they are responsible for doing so or not, devote themselves actively to losing their cerebral equilibrium, either because the environment is unfavorable or because they themselves do everything that is needed to make their brain sick and also contribute toward making others lose their equilibrium in various ways, notably by all the educational mistakes they make with young people? The neurophysiologist then realizes that everything he would like to advise as a result of what he knows about the brain is completely in accordance with the intuitions and reflections of moralists – not pharisaical and casuistic morality but the morality of involvement and personal reflection in the service of what is human. He wonders, therefore, whether his role is not to bring to the moralist, who is so often disputed in the name of the various philosophies and beliefs, an objective confirmation; in this way a commonly held *natural morality,* * with tolerance for various metaphysical choices, would have a scientific basis and become in men's eyes an indispensable asset. This morality of the *use of the brain,* this superior form of mental hygiene, is of capital importance today, in the face of the deranging influences of modern life and the possibilities of cerebral manipulation. It is up to neurophysiology to tell us precisely what a normal brain is and what must be done to keep it normal. Without this, all the progress of civilization will come to nought and be dehumanizing because we will not have been wise and prudent enough and will have forgotten the conditions of our nature. One branch of medical science today protects factory and atomic workers. Another branch is trying to preserve our normal living conditions in astronautical rockets. When will a generalized form of medical science protect us from the modern world and from our insane undertakings in everyday life?

Sleep is the best way for the brain to rest. Therapeutic sleep cure.

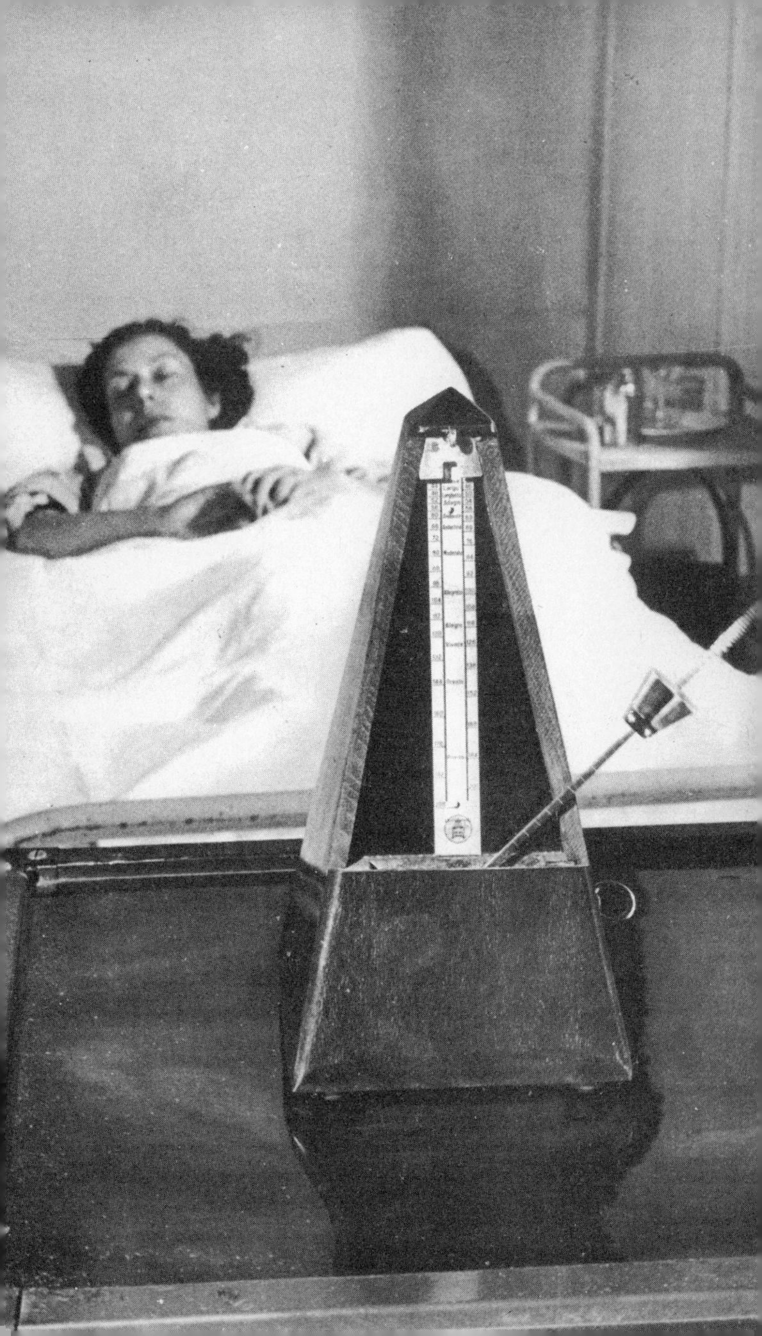

The disequilibrium of hectic modern life with its varied worries (which ought not to make us pine for the life of savages with its still graver disadvantages but rather incite us to humanize modern life) is the cause of today's principal sickness – *nervous fatigue,* nervous exhaustion, with its whole train of neuroses, fatigue, and various organic disturbances. Gone is that good old muscular fatigue that made us want to rest. The switchboard operator, the businessman, the housewife have the same nervous weakness; in spite of their apparently different lives, each leads a tense life, full of worries. Neurophysiology makes us understand the origin of this fatigue in a disequilibrium of the regulatory centers of the base of the brain – centers which are supposed to guarantee the wise use of the body in spite of all kinds of disequilibrium, regulatory centers of the brain, centers of the instinctive and emotional life. Nervous fatigue is a fatigue of regulatory functioning that shocks us *(stress *)* and makes rest necessary. Among the causes of disequilibrium and nervous fatigue that all the sleep therapies can improve, the noise of modern life must be given first rank. It is not, as people think, merely an unpleasant sensation, but a true nerve poison, because the auditory nervous impulses disturb the whole equilibrium of the basal regulatory centers. It is important to eliminate them.

The most useful thing about a knowledge of the brain is that it leads to a hygiene of the brain, which we cannot go into at length here. It has two fundamental aspects. First of all, it is necessary to try to obtain a normal brain through a well-balanced education and good hygiene. *A normal brain is a brain capable of reflection and freedom.* It is possible to indicate the educational conditions that will produce such a brain by avoiding as much as possible cerebral lesions, humoral disturbances (apparent defects resulting from endocrine disturbances), and, even more, important repressions of emotional shocks, which create unconscious complexes and neuroses, as psychoanalysis has clearly shown. One must avoid both the failures of *repressive* authoritarian education and the no less important failures of liberal education, which causes neuroses by the *unleashing* of instincts and the human inadequacy of the person who lacks will power and real freedom; for freedom is not the possibility of doing just anything, but the knowledge of what is appropriate and good.

Similarly, in adult life, we ought to know all the factors that contribute to mental disequilibrium – that is, what we should avoid. It is noteworthy that equilibrium in the case of all these factors – physical as well as psychological and social – demands an *optimum* and that excesses, whether positive or negative, are equally unbalancing. There are, for example, disturbances because of an excess or a deficiency of oxygen, but there are also the disturbances of an oppressed individual who cannot fully develop his personality and at the same time the neurosis of a tyrant, of the oppressor who has gone beyond human limits and is no longer normal. There can be no social equilibrium except that based on *complementary equality* and this is so because of the very laws of our brain. Social justice becomes an obligation of cerebral hygiene. This is still more true in the human sexual relationship, which should be first of all a human social relationship. Reflection on the subject of human cerebral sexuality is very enlightening as far as morality is concerned and fully confirms the opinions of the Christian moralists.

But, in order to be normal, in order to preserve a normal brain, it is not enough merely to keep from us everything that unbalances the brain. *We can make ourselves sick simply by refusing to act like men.* One cannot declare that everything that men do is normal and human on the mere basis of *statistics.* * This is one of the most important conclusions provided by neurophysiology of the brain. From the natural point of view, evil, or sin, or vice, is unbalancing because it willfully imitates that cerebral disintegration which is called neurosis. It is a disintegration of the brain, a nonhuman way of using it, and it leads us to a kind of neurosis.

We cannot be normal if we use the possibilities of cerebral control badly. Someone who buries himself in the instinctive or emotional excesses of sensuality or aggressiveness is not a real man; he reaches the point of using only his lower brain, the one which is closest to an animal's. Nor is that man normal who, refusing to reflect, acts automatically by conforming or systematically refusing to conform. It is necessary to have acquired good habits, but we must not passively accept what our environment gives us; we must reflect on the human value of our acts. The moralist gives all this advice, but he is no longer heeded by the emancipated world of technique and science, which does not see the objective necessity of his advice.

Neurophysiology confirms it by showing us that the command to love one's neighbor as oneself is the prescription for good cerebral equilibrium, the best use of the prefrontal lobe, that human superbrain.

Another valuable contribution made by the neurophysiological point of view in the field of natural morality is that it obliges us to have a *dynamic view* of human equilibrium, one that always includes an historical dimension. There is no such thing as static human equilibrium. The brain's equilibrium can be obtained only in the dynamism of a struggle against the unceasing tendencies toward disequilibrium, only by uninterrupted effort and progress. It is not placid and satisfied adaptation to an inhuman environment. But someone who has become adapted and whose habits have made happiness possible for him can suffer greatly if these habits are changed, even for the better, when the centers of his social life are destroyed.

At the outset, man presents only potentialities, which he may or may not realize in his individual history. To be a man with a normal brain is to be *fully adult*. This historical perspective also concerns humanity and its progress. Not everything is progress; progress lies in the complete development of the potentialities of human nature. Innumerable factors, influencing the human brain as the organ of progress, have built up in the past a history which, taken as a whole, has a *meaningful direction*, the improved use of the brain, the rise of consciousness, of freedom, of love. This is the undertaking that we must freely continue to pursue if the destiny of humanity is to be normal.

Let us not dream about some *superman* with a larger brain resulting from a spontaneous mutation or a technical invention. Serious arguments show that, with man, biological evolution has reached a summit where evolution is continued in social history. It is no longer a question of organic improvement, but of improvement in the collective use of the potentialities of individual brains, the organs of culture. How far we still are from using them or even from understanding them today! The greatest scientist and the primitive savage have the same brain; they are equally human, with their philosophical, religious, and esthetic concerns, their love, and their thirst for happiness, but what a difference there is in the development of these potentialities, thanks to culture and all kinds of educational conditioning! The savages of the Orinoco admire and understand Mozart; their technical inadequacy has prevented any potential Mozart among them from realizing himself. Instead of dreaming about a superman and risking the creation first of all of monsters, let us work toward the *humanization of humanity,* toward that *complementary equality* between races and cultures, all of which should attain their own adult status, so that men of talent and genius will not be forever lost because of the environmental circumstances of their earliest years which will have doomed them to lead a vegetative existence as unskilled laborers or savages in the primitive forest. Even today, the greatest injustice is still that all men not only cannot fully develop all their cerebral potentialities because of the cultural conditions of their class or people, but even lose these potentialities. It is a serious error to attribute too much to heredity.

Idealism and materialism

In our discussion of current tendencies in the neurophysiology of the human brain, which is a rapidly expanding science, we have shown that it would be a false kind of objectivity to want to limit ourselves to the standard scientific level. Today a neurophysiologist's reflections necessarily have a philosophical value and are connected with all human problems. The reason is that, now that technical improvements enable us to penetrate the inmost functioning of the organ of thought and consciousness, that thought and that consciousness can no longer remain outside the scope of our investigations. The function of the neurophysiologist who consents to pursue his task to its limit and to ask himself questions about the human role of nervous impulses, excitations, and inhibitions thus becomes most important to the development of a new *scientific humanism*, along the main line of traditional humanism. In doing so, the modern neurophysiologist is thus merely following the example of earlier philosophers such as Descartes or the materialist philosophers of the eighteenth century who tried to understand the relationship between the brain and thought, though they did so at a time when cerebral neurology was in its infancy.

Neurophysiology is a *science that has a bearing on philosophy*, but that is no reason for it to become an all-embracing scientism explaining everything about man. It does indeed concern itself with *all of man, but in a partial aspect*, namely the cerebral aspect, which is an important part of the material, organic aspect of being. This does not in the least do away with the other aspects, the psychological or sociological aspect. Knowing everything about the brain will no more rule out psychology than the scientific analysis of beauty will rule out its esthetic aspect and eliminate visual enjoyment of a woman.

Similarly, neurophysiology, in spite of what a number of philosophers have believed in the past, *does not make any particular metaphysical choice obligatory*. Although philosophical reflection on the nature of being benefits from the biological knowledge of being, it cannot be reduced to that knowledge. Each specific kind of philosophic research has its own technique. To this day, we go on living with two false philosophical conceptions about the relationship between those two constituent principles of man, soul and body. The materialists think that, by explaining man materially, science has proved that spirit is produced by matter, that only the body exists, and that at death everything is finished. Many idealists, affirming the independent existence of the temporarily incarnated spirit or soul, think that the body is a material mechanism in the service of the spirit and that, under these conditions, the spirit lives on after the death of the body. These metaphysical hypotheses may have troubled the minds of reseachers but they nevertheless stimulated neurological research. The problem was to find the soul or its site. It was, in short, a kind of "materialism" both on the part of the materialists, who materialized the spirit, and on the part of the idealists, who wanted to locate its position.

Another debate was based on the relationship between

animals and man. Are they similar or are they different? In spite of biological appearances, is man truly of a different nature, and is he alone endowed with an immortal spirit? A complete lack of objectivity as a result of metaphysical prejudice brought together materialists (who regarded both animals and men as machines) and idealists (who claimed that the animal alone is nothing but a machine). How do things stand today? Progress made by neurophysiology enables us to understand a little better, and certain materialist or idealist philosophic positions have become untenable.

Spirit is not a material product. It is a particular process which results from the over-all functioning of the brain and which cannot be localized or isolated. What we identify as spiritual has two aspects, its specific psychological aspect and its cerebral aspect. Modern *dialectical materialism* clearly recognizes this by its struggle against the errors of the old, so-called *mechanistic* materialism. The brain is not a machine activated from the outside by a separate spirit. The soul cannot be found with a scalpel; it is *immanent* * in the brain. Reflective consciousness is an aspect of a cerebral process which makes it possible to direct conduct and thought. The human brain and the animal brain are not identical; man has a *cerebral originality*, characterized by super-complexity. Therefore, man does not have a kind of monkey's brain activated by a human spirit; his brain is proportionate to his spirit. The old-time materialists minimized the human psychism; those of today do not do this, but that does not mean that they have become true idealists. For them it is a property of the brain, which is true; but such an observation is not the same thing as the materialist contention that it is *nothing but* a property of the brain.

Comparative neurophysiology shows both similarities and differences between animals and man, the latter occupying *first place*. We can describe the progress that actually took place in the evolution from unicellular animals to man. There is *no life without psychism*. The amoeba, a living creature, is closer to us than the robot. The cell, which is a small world by itself, has an elementary interiority that is shown by its integrated behavior, a true inferior psychism, *bioconsciousness*. Let us be careful with words.

The presence of an amoeba in the world and reflective human consciousness have apparently nothing in common; but it is a question of *analogous* considerations, for we find all the stages between the two correlated with the development of the nerve centers. Man would have no consciousness if he were not a living being. There is *no psychism without life.* What the amoeba needs to have a real consciousness is a brain. The question is one of a *difference in complexity* between two beings. Today, therefore, we can define a *biological aspect of human nature.* Is it different from animal nature? Certainly, and between animal and man there is an important margin in which quantitative complexification conditions new qualities, as neurophysiology shows.

Neurophysiology, which forces materialism toward *realism,* does the same to idealism, but it is not sufficiently realized that while idealism *distinguishes* body and soul in man, it by no means necessitates making of them two *separate,* interacting realities. Although this idealist position – the one held by Plato and Descartes – is a widespread prejudice, it is nonetheless opposed to true realistic idealism, the kind Aristotle passed on to his Arabian, Jewish, and Christian successors, such as Avicenna, Averroës, Maimonides, and Thomas Aquinas. Here the existential unity of man is not denied. The soul takes shape in the body and can no more be separated from it than the form of a statue can be separated from its material. What the biologist analyzes is not the body, but the human being, the animated body, the animated brain. Upon death, what remains in the absence of life is not a body but a cadaver. This unified philosophy, which also recognized the basic analogy between man and animals, identifying the difference between inanimate things, animals, and men as a progress in organization and information (that is, a difference in degree of intellect, true spirit existing only in man), is perfectly in accordance with modern neurophysiology. What science describes – all those integrated material processes in which the only thing that counts is a dynamic organization superimposed upon changing elements, in which what is spiritual is the mode of existence enjoyed by the whole – can be transposed directly into a dialectical materialist philosophy, but it also can be seen as the material aspect of the Aristotelian and Thomistic philosophic analysis. The soul is immanent in the organism and manifests itself only in its unified harmony there where the cerebral structures make possible its *emergence* * in the guidance of conduct.

Thus neurophysiology, which is not a science of the body but of the human being, leaves us free to reflect on what this human being is in and of *himself,* whether simply an organized body of which the spirit is an aspect, or incarnated spirit. Materialists and idealists are beginning to agree about the organic aspect of man. They should also affirm his more complex way of being, which depends not only on the brain but on that possibility of having a brain which is provided, as early as the egg, by *living human matter.* But this complexity, which objectively demonstrates the superior integration and therefore the soul, does not make it necessary to believe that this soul has a nature and a destiny different from the animal soul. However, it cannot in the least prevent us from believing this for other valid reasons. The neurophysiologist moves about in the *infrastructures* of human beings, the basements; these differ, depending on whether they belong to a suburban cottage, a five-story house, or a skyscraper, but it is impossible to know from this how many stories the skyscraper has. All psychological processes depend on the brain and have a cerebral aspect, but this does not mean that they have only this aspect. Consciousness is not an epiphenomenon; it is also a cerebral phenomenon; but *is it only that?*

Because it is knowledge of the human body, neurophysiology finds its own limits in the fact that its point of view is partial and does not permit it to settle certain essential problems. It would be inconsistent, therefore, for it to be all-encompassing; it leaves a way open for *philosophic reflection.* The common error of materialists is that they are scientists in the sense of believing that the scientific explanation is enough; the common mistake of idealists is to seem to believe them by dreading the scientific explanation and by believing that the authentic mystery is what science does not explain, whereas the comprehensibility of a world that is not absurd ought to be the best argument for idealism.

We are becoming more and more idealistic, but while

some are willing to follow their philosophical reflections on this idealism and its nature to their natural conclusion, others are satisfied with elementary philosophical reflections on science. What they say is correct but is only apparently materialistic, philosophically speaking. In the last analysis, therefore, true knowledge of the true nature of the human spirit will always depend on our free reflection. Our role here is to show that *neurophysiology leaves us free*. However, it seems to us that, once we have thrust aside the false problems of materialized thought or of the soul conceived of as something foreign to the body, there appears to be a striking convergence between these two paths of investigation, modern science and Thomistic philosophy. The harmony we have pointed out between human neurophysiology and traditional natural morality is also impressive. When we reflect on the potentialities of our brain compared to the animal brain, is there not something in its ability to think abstractly, in its aptitude in the fields of logic, concepts, philosophy, metaphysics, art, and religion, that reveals a different kind of nature, in spite of the fact that animals have also to their credit some very slight achievements in some of these domains? Is not this quantitative complexification which seems to furnish new qualities – this lesser something which seems to engender a greater something – an argument in favor of the rational philosophic explanation; that is, the explanation according to which it is not that the lesser something is creative, but that it is superanimated, that it contains, essentially, a new contribution? Is the human ability to reflect only a *cerebral emergence* * somewhat superior to what an animal has, or does not this mastery immanent in cerebral mechanisms mean that what is immanent has a nature that is its own, and is transcendent * – that it is a genuine spirit? One could thus develop a whole series of *arguments, not proofs,* that seem to favor, from the scientific point of view, the idealist hypothesis. But these arguments carry small weight for anyone who has not reflected on all the other arguments for idealism and faith which are not of a scientific nature and which give the believer his certitude. The convergence of neurophysiology and Thomism (naturally, we are considering Thomism here only in connection with the question of the relationship between the soul and the body) ought to incite us to give them serious consideration. According to Teilhard de Chardin, the great biologist who was at the same time a great believer, human equilibrium, the secret of happiness, that equilibrium which lies in the harmony of a brain in a fully human situation, depends on a triple integration, a triple love: *to be centered on oneself, to decenter oneself on someone else, to supercenter oneself on someone greater than oneself*. Although it is certain that idolizing a man is unbalancing for the person idolized as well as for the idolater, it seems likely that the human need for an ideal is better provided for, cerebrally, in a dialogue with a transcendent ideal that would still be Personal and Love. The realistic and tragic optimism of Teilhard, which is confirmed by the psychological arguments of Chauvin, seems to tell us that a humanity limited by death – both that of the individual and that of the species (and space travel will not change anything in this respect) – might perhaps be driven to disgust with life, especially because the technical world would seem to be despiritualizing. Making of faith a useful and equilibrium-producing motivation for human behavior is a curious but interesting psychophysiological confirmation of the salutary role it plays.

Short Guide to the Brain

ACETYLCHOLINE
Substance released at the end of certain nerve fibers (parasympathetic, voluntary nerve, nerve centers) by the nervous impulse for the transmission of the command to the innervated element. These fibers are said to be cholinergic.

ADIADOCHOKINESIA
Inability to execute correctly precise successive movements, as a result of losing the control of motor co-ordination in diseases of the cerebellum. The patient can no longer "move like a puppet."

ADRENALINE
Hormone produced by the medullosuprarenal gland. It has the same effects as the orthosympathetic nerves. This can be explained by the fact that the sympathetic nervous impulse releases adrenaline for the transmission of the command. Like acetylcholine, it is a chemical mediator of the impulse (adrenergic nerves).

AFFECTIVITY
Innate capacity to feel emotions; unconscious automatism, manifested by organic reactions, which is directed by the hypothalamus. It sets up a secondary echo in the brain, making us aware of the emotion. Three kinds: neutral (attention, interest, surprise), agreeable, and disagreeable.

ANALGESIC
Substance that suppresses general pain by acting upon the nerve centers.

ANENCEPHALUS
Monster born without a brain or with only the rudiments of one.

ANESTHETICS
Substances which suppress sensitivity; the general anesthetics act by stopping the functioning of the upper centers: anesthetic sleep or narcosis.

ANGIOGRAPHY
Radiography of vessels after injection of a substance that is opaque to X rays.

ANTHROPOIDS
The higher monkeys (chimpanzee, gorilla, orang-utan) whose brains are more like the human brain than those of any other extant animals; highly specialized creatures (tree-dwelling). They are not our ancestors, but rather distant cousins descended from common ancestors at the beginning of the Tertiary period.

APHASIA
Loss of speech resulting from cerebral lesion. Two major types: Broca's motor aphasia or anarthria, a kind of apraxia (inability to co-ordinate for articulation; preservation of inner language); Wernicke's sensorial aphasia (diffuse lesions disturbing inner language, particularly in its command of volitional evocation, although articulation is correct).

ATTENTION
Second level of consciousness which narrows the range of one's alertness to what one is interested in (affective aspect).

AUTOSCOPY
Doubling hallucination; it is positive if the image of one's body is seen as an external double, negative if one's image disappears from a mirror.

AXON
Part of the neuron consisting of a single nerve fiber conducting nervous impulsions away from the cell body. Axons differ in length and diameter. The smallest are gray, the largest white because of the myelin sheath that covers them.

BASE OF THE BRAIN
That part of the brain which is neither cerebral cortex nor white

matter, but the underlying formations: central ganglia, called basal ganglia (corpora striata, thalamus, hypothalamus), and, by extension, the mesencephalon and lower encephalic centers.

BEHAVIOR
The organism's reactions as a whole in response to certain signs in its environment and to certain internal states. These innate or acquired reactions, which make it possible to satisfy needs, are the external manifestation of psychism, the only object of scientific psychology. The neurophysiology of various kinds of behavior tries to differentiate them in respect to the most important thing about them, the level and state of the centers which govern them, distinguishing between automatic and deliberate kinds of behavior.

BIOCONSCIOUSNESS
Degree of consciousness of lower beings, term suggested by P. Chauchard to indicate both difference and similarity when compared to human consciousness.

BLOCKING REACTION
Replacement of alpha waves by more rapid and shorter waves as a result of desynchronization in sensorial or mental work (electroencephalograph).

BODY
Ambiguous word which is usually opposed to soul and designates the material part of man; neurophysiology, with its insistent stress on the brain as the corporeal organ of mind or spirit, shows that one cannot separate body from soul; the living being is living, organized, animated matter; the body is the material, organic aspect of being.

BRAIN
Somewhat imprecise term which designates the anterior part of the encephalon as opposed to the cerebellum and the brain stem. Synonymous with the cerebral hemispheres plus the cortex, white matter, and basal ganglia.

BRAIN STEM
Base of the encephalon: medulla oblongata, pons, mesencephalon.

BRAINWASHING
Metaphorical word describing the manipulation of the human brain by an ensemble of scientific procedures: weakening by tortures and hypnotics, destruction of habitual ways of thinking and training in new habits under the effect of fear of punishment and, particularly, satisfaction and rewards. Brutish way of treating man, which has nothing in common with the art of convincing and with reason, and which has only temporary effects. It can lead to serious psychiatric disturbances. Has nothing in common with a voluntary effort to submit one's brain to a kind of apprenticeship, as in painless childbirth.

CENTRAL GRAY NUCLEI
Part of the gray matter of the cerebral hemispheres making possible automatic types of behavior: the corpora striata, which serve a motor function, the thalami, which serve a sensory and coordinative function, and the hypothalamus, which is the regulatory center of the metabolisms, instincts, and affective life.

CEPHALIZATION
The concentration or initiation of the growth tendency at the head end of the embryo.

CEPHALIZATION
(coefficient of)
Figure calculated from the ratio established by Dubois between brain weight and body weight, making it possible to evaluate the comparative development of the brain in the various species independently of body weight. It determines the position of the isoneural lines in Lapicque's chart; the tiny cat and the huge tiger have the same coefficient. Man has the largest coefficient. It is no more than an imprecise approximation.

CEREBELLUM
Derived embryologically from the

upper and posterior part of the next-to-the-last encephalic ventricle (between the mesencephalon in front and the medulla oblongata behind) the lower and ventral part of which forms the pons, from which it is separated by the top of the fourth ventricle; the cerebellum is a large nervous organ located behind the brain and connected by three pairs of cerebellar peduncles behind the brain stem. It is comprised of a white center with gray nuclei and a gray cortex whose essential element is the neuron of Purkinje. Neither motor nor sensory, it is the organ of precision regulation of muscular tonus concerning positions and movements; it checks and improves the regulation provided by the centers of the mesencephalon, the pons, and the medulla oblongata. In man, an important part (neocerebellum) is devoted, in connection with the brain, to the harmony of volitional movements.

CEREBRAL CORTEX
Synonymous with gray cortex. The organ of psychism. The neocortex, which is peculiar to mammals, is to be distinguished from the primitive cortex of the rhinencephalon. The former has six unequally divided cellular layers, including the homotypical cortex of the zones of association and two kinds of heterotypical cortex, granular (granule cells, or sensory neurons) and agranular (pyramidal motor neurons). The latter has fewer and less distinct layers.

CEREBRAL HEMISPHERES
Anterior part of the encephalon, including an outer part separated into two lateral masses with superficial gray cortex and white fibers further in, and a single center formed by the right and left central gray nuclei joined together. The hemispheres are joined together by the corpus callosum. At the level of the central nuclei the hemispheres are connected with the brain stem. Each hemisphere has a cavity, the lateral ventricle, communicating with a central cavity between the central nuclei, the third ventricle. The hemispheres, which are divided into several lobes, are the organ of psychism and the various kinds of behavior.

CEREBRAL LOCALIZATIONS
We may localize in the brain motor neurons of execution and co-ordination, neurons of sensorial reception and co-ordination, certain neuronic circuits of physiological importance (memory, attention, mastery, etc.). We do not localize either thought or consciousness, which are the result of an integrated, over-all functioning. Localized lesions in these zones produce paralyses, apraxias, anesthesias, agnosias, neurological disturbances of the brain. Psychiatric disturbances do not depend on localized lesions, but on an over-all physiological disturbance.

CEREBRAL PEDUNCLES
Bundles of white matter (notably pyramidal motor neurons) occupying the lower part of the mesencephalon and connecting the diencephalon and the pons.

CEREBROSPINAL FLUID
Fluid contained in the central cavities of the encephalon and the spinal cord and the peripheral meningeal spaces; it is a secretion having blood as a base. Its role is a hydrostatic one of support and protection. An excess of this fluid causes cranial hypertension, which squeezes the brain and prevents it from functioning well.

CHEMICAL MEDIATORS
Chemical substances released by the nervous impulse and transmitting its effects to the innervated element. See *acetylcholine* and *adrenaline*. The question of chemical mediation in the nerve centers is not yet well understood; there is a tendency to attribute inhibition to a chemical substance. The reticular formation is believed to have an important chemical activity.

CHRONAXY
Time of excitation required to obtain the threshold (minimum

reaction) with a current just double the minimum strength (rheobasis). This constant, suggested by Lapicque, makes it possible, with the help of an electric excitation, to express in figures the rapidity of any cell and its variations. The chronaxy diminishes when the element is excited and increases when it is slowed down. The chronaxies of the nerves vary under the effect of central excitations and inhibitions (subordination), thereby providing a convenient test for nervous equilibrium.

COMA

Pathological suspension of cerebral activity (loss of consciousness, psychism, volition) through neuronic poisoning; differs from physiological sleep.

COMPLEXIFICATION

Increase in organization which is not merely quantitative, such as simple complication, but an augmentation of value, the source of new qualities. Between monkeys and man there is cerebral complexification not because of a simple increase in the number of neurons but because this increase multiplies the possibilities of interconnection. Biological evolution shows numerous complications; there is no real complexification of being except in the brain's development.

CONDITIONED REFLEXES

The adjective *conditioned,* which is preferable to *conditional,* characterizes reflexes that are not absolute and innate, but that come about by repeated association of an indifferent signal with a signal that is meaningful from the outset. Training and education are the conditioning factors. Pavlov studied them scientifically and used them to discover the physiology of the brain, whose functioning consists in the acquisition of conditioned reflexes, notably those of language in the case of man.

CONSCIOUSNESS

From the neurophysiological point of view, one distinguishes several levels of consciousness: wakefulness (or sleep), consciousness of oneself, attention, verbalized reflective consciousness; finally the aptitude for making judgments and looking ahead (moral conscience). We are beginning to understand the nervous processes that condition them and that are aspects of self-regulation and cerebral integration.

CORPORA QUADRIGEMINA

Upper part of the mesencephalon. The anterior pair is the center of visual reflexes, the posterior pair of auditory reflexes. In the lower vertebrates, there is only one pair, called optic lobes, the roof (tectum) of which contains psychomotor centers.

CORPORA STRIATA

Outer portion of the central gray nuclei located at the center of the hemispheres and divided into the caudate nucleus and the lenticular nucleus. Only the inner third of the lenticular nucleus exists in the lower vertebrates. These are automatic motor nuclei. Trembling paralysis (Parkinson's disease) involves lesions of the corpora striata.

CORPUS CALLOSUM

Thick bundle of nerve fibers connecting the inside surfaces of the two cerebral hemispheres and making possible their co-ordination.

CYBERNETICS

From a Greek word meaning steersman, taken by Norbert Wiener from Plato and Ampère: comparative study of self-regulatory systems in machines, the brain, and societies. Cybernetics has created machines that have their own behavior: Grey Walter's electronic turtles, Ashby's homeostat, models of nervous functioning.

CYTO-ARCHITECTURE

Science of the structures and neuronic connections of the brain. Draws up atlases of the brain, with numbered areas.

DENDRITES

Fibers which are usually numerous, ramified, and relatively short, often without myelin, along which nerve impulsions move toward the body of the neuron, into which they insert themselves. Sometimes a single, long, myelinated dendrite contributes toward the formation of nerves (peripheral fibers of the sensory neurons of the spinal ganglion, whose axon connects the ganglion and the spinal cord).

DIASTASES (OR ENZYMES)

Substances produced by cells which by their presence in small quantity make possible cellular chemism at normal temperature; some of them, such as cholinesterase, which destroys acetylcholine, play an important part in the nervous system.

DIENCEPHALON

Part of the base of the brain located around the third ventricle and including on its sides the thalamus, in its upper part the epithalamus connected with the epiphysis (or pineal body), and in its lower part the hypothalamus connected with the hypophysis (or pituitary gland).

EDEMA (CEREBRAL)

Circulatory disorder involving a draining of plasma from the blood vessels and bringing about disturbances through compression and lack of neuronic alimentation; frequent complication in brain surgery.

EGG

First stage of the individual, resulting from the fusion of paternal and maternal gametes. The egg develops in the uterus of mammals; it is laid by birds.

ELECTRIC SHOCK

Epileptic attack involving loss of consciousness brought about by electricity for therapeutic reasons in psychiatry.

ELECTRODE

Metallic conductor placed in contact with a center, a nerve, or a muscle, either directly or on the skin nearby, in order to record its electric activity or to send a current into it. Microelectrodes are microscopically thin needles that can enter a neuronic cell body. Electrodes can be permanently placed in the brain without disturbing its activity. To make it possible to study electric activity, the current registered by the electrodes is amplified by electronic amplifiers and recorded by an oscillograph.

ELECTRO-ENCEPHALOGRAPHY

Method of recording encephalograms. The total electric activity of the brain is noted by means of external electrodes at various points on the scalp. If electrodes are placed in the brain, the method is called electrocorticography.

EMBRYO

Stage of development between the second and the eighth week of pregnancy in human beings, when the organs and the human form begin to take shape.

EMERGENCE

This philosophical term designates the appearance of new qualities by complexification. It is subject to interpretation: materialists interpret it as being a property of matter; idealists see in it the organic, material aspect of a spiritual factor of another order (transcendent) which complexifies matter. Example: emergence of the human psychism thanks to cerebral complexification.

ENCEPHALON

Ensemble of the higher nerve centers contained in the skull, as opposed to the spinal cord. Origin of the cranial nerves. Is divided into brain stem, cerebellum, and brain, the part of the stem between the cerebellum and the brain being the cerebral isthmus. The brain stem is divided, from back to front, into the medulla oblongata, the pons, and the mesencephalon with the cavities of the fourth ventricle and the aqueduct of Sylvius. In front of the mesencephalon, the diencephalon (thalamus, hypothalamus, and third ventricle) joins the base of the telencephalon (corpora striata) to form the basal ganglia of the brain; the rest of the telencephalon makes up the cerebral hemispheres with the cavities of the lateral ventricles.

ENDOCRINE GLAND
Gland which secretes hormones into the blood. The hypothalamus has an endocrinal activity.

EQUILIBRIUM
There is no stable or static nervous or psychic equilibrium; equilibrium is an unstable state, a constant struggle against disequilibrium, a tiring self-regulation that is easily upset.

ERGOTHERAPY
Re-education of the mentally sick by a kind of work adapted to their sickness. Made possible by soothing medicaments. (Paul Sivadon.)

EVOKED POTENTIALS
Nervous impulsions recorded at the level of the neurons – for example, those of the cerebral cortex – in response to an excitation of just any part of the body or of some other part of the nerve centers. They make it possible to study anatomical interrelations and cerebral localizations in a living subject.

EXCITABILITY
Capacity of living matter to react to excitants, physical or chemical variations in the outer environment to which it is sensitive; the laws of excitability concern living matter; the most convenient excitant is the electric excitant. This is natural because every excitation is an electric discharge from the cellular surface, automatically bringing about activation. Excitability varies according to the state of the cell.

EXCITATION
State of hyperactivity of the neuron, which is more excitable and reacts more, and in an accelerated way; this state involves a depolarization (diminution of the surface charge).

FATIGUE
Diminution of the functional aptitudes of an organ or of the entire organism which has been poisoned by excessively intense or excessively prolonged functioning; is accompanied by a characteristic sensation. The most important fatigue today is nervous fatigue, the disequilibrium of the nerve centers that regulate organic and cerebral harmony, bringing about organic and psychological disturbances; these centers are indeed called into play excessively by all the external, internal, and psychic shocks (see this word) of modern life.

FEELING
Awareness of an affective state.

FETUS
Period of intra-uterine life from the eighth week until birth; construction of the organs and acquisition of an elementary kind of behavior.

FISSURE
Groove separating cerebral lobes: fissure of Rolando, Sylvian fissure.

FOVEA
Central part of the retina, the organ of precise daylight vision and color vision. It is made up exclusively of cones connected directly with the brain.

FREEDOM
For the neurophysiologist, freedom is a property of the human brain, the possibility a normal brain has of mastering its determinisms, choosing among them, inventing a more appropriate form of behavior; it is a result of the physiology of reflective consciousness, which gives man the power to judge himself. Freedom does not lie in the nonexistent fissures of determinisms;

it is a superior determinism – not a transcendent, magic power to do just anything, but the recognition of the fact that what is good is that which produces equilibrium and that evil results in disequilibrium; that therefore we must be *men* if we want to avoid pathology. In order to free man, it is necessary first of all to give him a normal brain that is capable of freedom, and then to teach him what he must do in order not to lose it.

GANGLION (*pl.* ganglia)
Small, elementary nerve center: sympathetic ganglion, sensory spinal ganglion, ganglia of invertebrates. The central gray nuclei are sometimes called central ganglia. The nerve ganglia are not to be confused with the lymphatic ganglia commonly called "glands."

GENERAL SENSITIVITY
Under this term are grouped the sensitivities that do not come from specialized senses, but from the skin, muscles, tendons, and internal organs, and that are received in the parietal zone – in particular, the various modalities of taction and palpation.

GERM
Beginning period of development from egg to embryo (second week), when the cells divide and the adnexa and germ layers become distinct.

GESTALT PSYCHOLOGY
Psychology which correctly affirms that the over-all functioning of the brain causes new properties to appear which are not in analytic reflexology. The error of this psychology was to cut itself off from physiology and to fail to see that there exists a physiology of the integration of reflexes.

GNOSIA
Physiological term closely related to the psychological term *perception*. Co-ordination of the elementary sensorial messages making possible the recognition, for example, of an object or a word. It is taken care of by centers close to the centers of reception and depends on educative conditioned reflexes. Lesions cause agnosias such as astereognosis (loss of touch recognition) or verbal deafness or amusia. The agnosiac has lost none of his elementary sensitivity.

GRAY MATTER
Forms, with white matter, the nerve centers. It is of the greatest importance because it is the seat of the nerve cell bodies, the dendrites, and the innumerable synapses that connect the neurons. It is the inextricable network that is the seat of switchings and integration; it is for this reason that the gray cerebral cortex is the organ of psychism. Its grayness is due to the absence of myelin.

HALLUCINATIONS
Perception not founded upon objective reality; in neurophysiology, any nonphysiological excitation of the sensorial receptors, tracts, and centers is interpreted as coming from an external excitation.

HALLUCINATORY DRUGS
Certain chemical stupefacients cause hallucinations by exciting the brain; depending on the degree of poisoning, one is conscious or one's consciousness is disturbed and one sinks into dreams. Hashish and artificial paradises yesterday, peyotl and mescaline, derivatives of ergot (lysergine), or Mexican mushrooms (psilocybine) today.

HEALTH
Good organic condition. Mental health depends on the good functioning of the brain, not only from the point of view of its anatomophysiological equilibrium, but also from that of its correct use. It is based upon the physiological, psychological, and social human norm.

HEMIANOPSIA
Partial disappearance of the visual

field. Because of the structure of the optic tracts, lesions between the chiasma and the brain blind the corresponding parts of both retinas.

HEREDITY

That part in an individual which depends on the composition of the egg, especially the chromosomal structure; therefore both what comes from the parents and what is new (association of the two gametes or sexual cells). Identical twins (egg separated in two at its first division) have the same heredity. It is difficult to distinguish what depends on heredity from what depends on environmental influence. From conception on, there are disturbances which are not truly hereditary but depend, not on an anomaly of the chromosomes, but on an inferior quality of the sexual cells (alcoholism). Congenital disturbances (birth) are not all hereditary, but may come from a pathological intra-uterine development.

HIBERNATION

Physiological state of winter sleep in certain mammals such as the woodchuck. A complex nervous and hormonal regulation eliminates thermoregulation in winter; internal temperature drops, reducing cellular requirements and stopping activity without involving any damage to the cerebral neurons. This state is imitated in human artificial hibernation, in which the thermoregulatory centers are blocked by being poisoned with drugs; one thus suppresses states of shock and plunges the patient into a protective and restful coma by chilling.

"HOMINIZATION"

Biological process by which man appears through evolution. He emerges by successive stages in the group of Hominidae, only the last of which is true man. "Hominization" includes the standing position, which frees the hand and enlarges the skull, making possible an increase in the number of cerebral neurons, which is the essential characteristic of progress. At the same time, there is a considerable slowing-down in the rate of growth, which delays adulthood and favors apprenticeship, whereas the instincts are diminished. The individual evolution from egg to adult is a case of "hominization," with multiple possibilities of dehumanization.

HORMONES

Chemical substances with specific physiological effects, produced by the endocrine glands and secreted into the blood. Their activity regulates cellular functioning, particularly that of the neurons. In the hypothalamus there exist neurons that secrete hormones.

HYDROCEPHALUS

Condition resulting in a monster with a huge skull, the cerebral ventricles of which are distended by cerebrospinal fluid which fails to flow as the result of an obstruction of the aqueduct of Sylvius; the fluid compresses the cerebral cortex and prevents it, as in anencephalia, from developing. Reduced psychism.

HYGIENE (cerebral)

Since the brain is the organ of behavior and psychism, its sound equilibrium will depend not simply upon the ordinary hygiene concerning the physical conditions of life, but upon a psychological, moral, and social optimum. The psychosociologist ought to realize that he is a specialist in cerebral hygiene.

HYPERPNEA

Accelerated and deep breathing which decreases the amount of carbon dioxide in the blood and creates the state of excitation and contractures (tetany) identified with gaseous alkalosis. Is used in electroencephalography to modify the state of the brain and reveal latent epileptic states.

HYPNOSIS

Kind of sleep induced by certain procedures in sensitive subjects, during which the hypnotized subject remains in rapport with the hypnotizer, responsive to his suggestions. Simple suggestion is related to hypnosis, but without sleep. Studied first of all in cases of hysteria, and capable of being induced easily under the effect of hypnotics (narcoanalysis), hypnosis fell into disfavor but is regaining importance; certain methods of relaxation lead to hypnosis. The study of hypnosis is of great importance for the physiology of the brain.

HYPNOTICS
Chemical substances endowed with a depressive action on the brain, making it easier to go to sleep naturally. Whereas anesthetics suppress consciousness by poisoning, the action of hypnotics is to lower the brain's resistance to natural sleep. They too, however, are cerebral poisons which must be used with prudence. Example: barbiturates.

HYPNOTOXIN
Substance released in the brain during prolonged experimental insomnia (Piéron), responsible for cerebral lesions and death.

HYPOPHYSIS
Endocrine gland connected with the hypothalamus by the pituitary stalk and functioning in relation to this center. It is called the endocrinal brain because it regulates the functions of the other endocrine glands through stimulating hormones, playing an important role in psychosomatic equilibrium. It includes an anterior part, a real gland, the source of the growth hormone and of stimulating hormones (controlled chemically through the blood by the hypothalamus) and a nervous posterior part in which the hormones produced by certain hypothalamic neurons are stored.

HYPOTHALAMUS
Series of nuclei of gray matter located in the base of the brain (diencephalon) under the thalamus at the level of the floor of the third ventricle and connected with the hypophysis. They provide organic unity in the area of both the "life of nutrition" and of behavior: sympathetic and hormonal regulation of the metabolisms, elementary command of the automatic, instinctive kinds of behavior (nourishment, drinking, sexuality) and of affective reactions (attention, pain, pleasure). The superior regulation of these functions is taken care of by the primitive brain (rhinencephalon). Hypothalamic disturbances give birth in the brain to sensations of need (hunger, thirst) and to feelings; the brain masters the hypothalamic reactions and gives them moral causes (conditioning); it can also, in neuroses, throw the hypothalamus out of equilibrium (psychosomatic disturbances). Hypothalamic disequilibrium is the principal cause of nervous fatigue. All varieties of sedative therapy place the hypothalamus at rest. This center works in association with the reticular formation.

HYSTERIA
Mental disease involving a susceptibility to unconscious suggestion and to the inducement of hypnotic sleep, as well as psychosomatic disturbances.

IDEALISM
Philosophical doctrine which affirms the existence of the soul as a spiritual principle in man. The dualistic idealism of Plato and Descartes, which makes the soul act from the outside upon the corporeal mechanisms, is scientifically false; the unitary idealism of Aristotle and Thomas Aquinas *(hylemorphism)*, which does not separate the soul from the body – a body animated by an incarnate soul whose transcendence acts only through immanence – is scientifically acceptable.

IMAGE OF OUR BODY
Or: corporeal schema. Gnosic synthesis in the parietal zone of all the sensorial messages from the body. We have learned how to recognize our body and its cerebral image plays an important role in awareness (man's verbaliz-

ed reference to his neural self as I). See *autoscopy*.

IMAGES (thoughts by)

Pavlov's first signaling system: simple type of conditioned reflexes common to men and animals, as opposed to the second system, human verbalized thought. The psychological term image designates for the neurophysiologist cerebral structurations that are generalized throughout the brain, corresponding to the sensorial cerebral reflection of the world and of oneself, and that we can evoke in the brain in a completely inner way (imagination). The cerebral structures of the images provide the material basis of mental interiority.

IMMANENT

Philosophical term opposed to *transcendent*. A phenomenon is immanent when it is of the same order as the conditions of its manifestation. For materialists, the human soul is purely immanent in cerebral functions, of which it is not independent; for idealists, this is true of the animal soul, but the human soul is of another nature; it is transcendent. However, opposed to the conception that what is transcendent – soul or God – is a separate reality acting from the outside upon the world and the brain, is the realistic thesis (the only one compatible with science) that what is transcendent is not separate but is at the same time immanent, acting from within through the path of immanence, and this is what conceals it and makes it possible not to see its true dimension.

INHIBITION

The inverse of excitation. An inhibited neuron is not simply at rest; its functioning is braked, slowed down; it becomes less excitable, and its reaction to excitations is reduced. It is therefore cut off from functioning and remains in contact only with inhibited neurons. Inhibition depends on a surface superpolarization of the neuron.

INNATE

That which does not require education. Synonym: instinct. As opposed to what is acquired and conditioned.

INNER ENVIRONMENT

This was Claude Bernard's term for the organic environment in which our cells live and whose physical and chemical characteristics are kept constant by a regulatory system under any variable conditions, unless the latter are extreme. Blood is one of the important elements of this environment. Cerebral equilibrium is ensured by the stability of the inner environment.

INNER LANGUAGE

A property of the human brain, Pavlov's second signaling system. The conditioned reflexes of concrete signals are replaced by the signals of language. A tonal signal whose richness depends on the human cerebral aptitude for articulation (the inadequacy of an animal's brain makes it incapable of this) has become a human way of thinking because the verbal images have become autonomous cerebral structures that can be evoked automatically for their own sake, apart from any emission of sounds. Cerebral physiology makes distinctions among the localized aspects of language: motor aspect of the praxias which is disturbed in Broca's aphasia or anarthria (impossibility of articulating but preservation of inner language); sensorial aspect of the gnosias such as verbal deafness (agnosia) of inner language which is disturbed only in the case of extensive lesions (Wernicke's aphasia), in which the patient can articulate but can no longer find his words (volitional control of language has become impossible, but the unconscious verbalized automatisms of thought are preserved).

INSTINCT

Ordered, automatic succession of simple reflex kinds of behavior fulfilling a function that is important for the individual (alimentation) or the species (reproduction). Instincts depend on an innate aptitude of the hypothalamic centers to structure themselves in an adapted way when they are sensitized, notably by hormones or the state of the inner environment; a signal from the outer environment which would have no effect otherwise then becomes a reflex source of the kind of behavior it normally evokes. Modern scientific study (Lorenz, Tinbergen) has shown their resemblance to conditioned reflexes (apart from the fact that instincts are innate).

INSULIN
Pancreatic hormone that decreases the amount of sugar in the blood, causing a coma that is used in psychiatry.

INTEGRATION
For an organism or for the brain, the fact of not being the seat of independent functions, but of functioning as a unified, harmonized, and self-regulated whole. Integration is based on certain processes and depends on certain organs, but it can be materialized only if one takes a synthetic, over-all view. The physiology of consciousness depends on the cerebral integration of impulsions, reflexes, etc. Integration leads to a superior kind of unity which goes beyond the unities integrated.

INTELLIGENCE
Is not to be opposed to instinct, but signifies the aptitude for personal control of the instinctive and acquired reflexes, making it possible to use one's experience for better-adapted behavior; is proportionate to cerebral complexity, which in man conditions a superior type of abstract intelligence objectively different from an animal's concrete intelligence.

"INTELLIGENCE PILLS"
Journalistic term for glutamic acid, which helps the functioning of neurons in abnormal cases, but does not in the least increase normal memory or intelligence.

ISTHMUS (cerebral)
Portion of the brain stem between the cerebellum and the brain; essentially the mesencephalon.

LATENT LIFE
Suspension of the usual signs of life (breathing, circulation, etc.) without death, proving the possibilities of reanimation (it is incorrect to speak of this as resurrection). This state comes about as a means of struggling against desiccation, cold, etc. (cysts, seeds, lower animals that become reviviscent). A similar state is seen in mammals in the case of artificial hibernation; lowering the temperature to 0 degrees Centigrade makes it possible to eliminate temporarily breath and circulation requirements. The brain is completely stopped (coma) but does not suffer.

LEFT-HANDEDNESS
Innate preponderance of the right brain (left hand) over the left brain, less frequent than right-handedness, which is the reverse. The left-handed person has his language centers in the side opposite the one where most people have theirs. One must not try to change true left-handers, because this may cause cerebral conflicts resulting in stuttering and varied psychosomatic disturbances. Sometimes the left-handed person writes as if in a mirror.

LIFE
Physicochemical properties of living matter that ensure physiological and psychological functions; their specificity depends on the complexity of living matter and. as an ultimate guardian, its integration in the individual.

LOBE (Cerebral)
Important zones of the cerebral hemispheres marked off by grooves or fissures. On the outer surface the frontal lobe in front, the parietal lobe above, the occipital lobe behind, the temporal lobe beneath; in the Sylvian fissure the insular lobe. On the inner surface, the continuation of

the lobes of the outer surface and, around the central nuclei, the limbic convolution, formed by the cingulum above and the temporal lobe of the hippocampus below, which constitutes the most important lobe of the primitive brain, or rhinencephalon, where the olfactory formations terminate.

LOBOTOMY, LEUKOTOMY

Psychosurgical operation intended to destroy the prefrontal region or disconnect it on both sides; used in cases of psychiatric disturbances in order to restore behavioral equilibrium.

Lobotomy is a general term; *leukotomy* refers to cutting the white matter and *topectomy* to ablations of the gray matter. Increasingly limited operations are being performed, depending on the disturbances to be corrected. A lobotomy is a serious cerebral mutilation; it may suppress disequilibrium, but it does so at the price of diminishing the personality. Fortunately, the use of tranquilizers has reduced the number of cases where it is indicated.

LOVE

Ambiguous word indicating one's relation to oneself, to one's sexual partner, to other people, to values, and to God. It designates either an inferior instinctive and affective reaction (libido) of an irrational order, or the supreme quality of human consciousness, which surpasses reason without being contrary to it. Dissociated between flesh and spirit, love regains its unity thanks to neurophysiology, which reveals to us the two nervous levels of love – the lower level of the hypothalamus and the rhinencephalon, the higher level of the prefrontal brain.

MATERIALISM

Philosophical doctrine which makes spirit a property of matter, denying the separate existence and the immortality of the soul as well as the existence of God. There are two types of materialism: mechanistic materialism, according to which thought is a material product that can be localized and isolated in the brain (an opinion which is scientifically false); and dialectical materialism, according to which thought is an aspect of cerebral functioning which cannot be either localized or separated (an opinion which is scientifically possible). Philosophic materialism is generally identified with the scientific conception of the cerebral conditions of human thought, which is perfectly in accordance with Thomistic idealism – which proclaims the inseparability of the brain and the soul which animates it, the fact that the transcendent soul is immanent in the brain.

MEDULLA OBLONGATA

Also called the rachidian bulb or myelencephalon. Last part of the encephalon located between the cervical medulla and the pons, and connected with the cerebellum by the inferior cerebellar peduncles. Origin of numerous cranial nerves which have their motor and sensory nuclei here, particularly the parasympathetic nuclei of the pneumogastric system. This is what accounts for the medulla's role in swallowing, speaking, and regulating the heart, blood pressure, and breathing (without which life is impossible). Seat of centers that regulate muscular tonus. The motor and sensory paths pass through it.

MENINGES

Protective membranes of the nervous system containing cerebrospinal fluid. The outer one is the dura mater, the middle one the arachnoid, and the inner one, which adheres to the nervous tissue, is the pia mater.

MESENCEPHALON

Middle part of the encephalon, making up the upper part of the brain stem and the cerebral isthmus. Traversed by the aqueduct of Sylvius, with the two pairs of quadrigeminal bodies in its upper part and at its base the cerebral peduncles, which are bundles of white matter connecting the brain with the lower centers. It owes its importance in the regulation of muscular tonus and of nervous and especially cerebral functioning (wakefulness) to the red nucleus and to the reticular formation occupying its center with the oculomotor nuclei.

METABOLISM
Chemical activity required for the maintenance of life and including energy-releasing destructions, and constructive or reparative syntheses. The metabolism is weak when the body is at rest and increases when it is active. It is subject to the influence of regulatory factors and is activated particularly by the thyroid hormone. It is measured by the intensity of respiration or by the corresponding release of heat either in a cell or in the organism as a whole.

METACHRONOSIS
Change of chronaxy.

MICROELECTRODE
See *electrode*.

MUSCULAR TONUS
Varying degree of tension of the muscle under the influence of its nerve, regulated by centers which adapt it to needs (positions and movements) according to information supplied by muscular sensitivity to tension.

MYELIN
Whitish, phosphorated fat which forms an isolating sheath around the large sensory and motor nerve fibers ("life of relation").

NARCOANALYSIS
Chemical hypnosis; in certain doses, hypnotics diminish resistance and the subject confesses what he wants to hide (truth serum); actually, this method chiefly increases suggestibility. Method that makes an accelerated psychoanalysis possible. The effect is strengthened if one gives in addition an excitant such as benzedrine.

NARCOSIS
Cerebral poisoning leading to loss of consciousness in anesthetic sleep, used in surgery.

NATURAL MORALITY
Moral behavior adapted to man's nature and psychobiological equilibrium. Will be regarded as a biological fact by materialists, and justified metaphysically by idealists.

NEED
Uncoercible periodic tendency to accomplish a physiological act or a kind of behavior. Need depends on an unconscious sensitizing of the basal centers; it is conscious only secondarily, through its repercussion on the cerebral cortex. Need causes first of all an activation (appetitive behavior) and secondarily a specific kind of behavior that varies according to the nature of the need.

NEOCORTEX
As opposed to the rhinencephalon, the portion of the cerebral cortex which is peculiar to mammals and man. The brain of reflective psychism and control.

NERVE
Aggregate of numerous nerve fibers connecting the centers and the organs; nerves are motor, sensory, or mixed. We distinguish between the cranial or rachidian nerves of the "life of relation" and the sympathetic nerves which spread out in plexuses.

NERVE CENTERS
Grouping of nerve cells, interconnected in complex networks, forming the points of departure and arrival of the nerve fibers. The simplest are the sympathetic or sensory ganglia. The principal part of man's nerve centers forms the encephalorachidian system (encephalon and spinal cord).

NERVOUS IMPULSE (wave of)
Or, better, *nervous impulsion* (pulsations when there are several). Phenomenon which is conducted by the excited nerve fiber and which is the basic element of

nervous functioning. Sensorial messages and motor orders as well as cerebral functioning depend on nervous pulsations. Nerve activation is a complex physicochemical process, a reaction of living matter, the conduction of a self-excitation. The characteristics of the impulse depend on the state of the living matter of the fiber. From the functional point of view, the principal phenomenon is the electric wave propagated by depolarization (spike), which is nervous impulsion in the strict sense of the term, the impulsion recorded by the oscillograph.

NEUROGLIA

Supporting tissue of the brain, of the same embryological origin as the neurons.

NEUROLEPTICS

Delay's expression to designate the drugs of which chlorpromazine (largactyl) is representative, and which calm the regulatory centers of the base of the brain without producing excitement or causing sleep. These drugs, used to counter anxiety and psychosomatic disturbances, have humanized asylums by making possible psychotherapy and ergotherapy.

NEURONS

Nerve cells. They are distinguished anatomically as multipolar, bipolar, and unipolar, depending on the number of their processes. They include a cell body, dendrites, and an axon. From the physiological point of view, we can list: the peripheral sensory neuron, which describes a T, whose cell body is in the spinal ganglion; the peripheral motor neuron of the anterior cornu of the medulla; the neuron of Purkinje of the cerebellum; the pyramidal or psychomotor neuron of volitional motoricity whose cell body is in the motor cortex and whose axon extends into the medulla; the granule cell (or esthesioneure), a cortical sensory neuron; etc.

NEUROSIS

As opposed to psychosis: psychological disorder without serious disturbance of consciousness, involving complexes repressed in the unconscious and factors of psychosomatic disturbances whose origin is attributed by neurophysiology to the cerebral conflict between excitation and inhibition.

NEUROSURGERY

Surgical operation on the nervous system, especially on the centers in order to section a tract, remove a tumor, etc. Neurosurgery of the brain is intended to suppress localized neurological disturbances, as opposed to psychosurgery, the goal of which is to restore equilibrium to the psychism.

NOETIC BRAIN

The brain of knowledge, language, and reasoning. As opposed to the rhinencephalon, the instinctive and affective brain, and to the prefrontal brain of control, it groups the sensorial and motor zones of the neocortex (posterior frontal, parietal, occipital, and temporal). Broadly speaking, our reasoning and thinking machine.

NOOSPHERE

Term used by Teilhard de Chardin, formed like *atmosphere* or *biosphere*. Union of all men in a personalizing community; that norm of human evolution which is not inevitable but must be willed. Opposed to totalitarian society and individualism.

NORM

Not what is the most frequent, but what is best adapted to natural laws, to the optimum of functioning.

NUTRITION (life of)

As opposed to "life of relation" (Bichat): the regulated ensemble of the internal functions that take care of cellular needs: breathing, digestion, circulation, excretion. The sympathetic system is the nervous system of the "life of nutrition."

OPTIC CHIASMA

Transitional joining under the brain of the two optic nerves, making possible the crossing of certain fibers toward the opposite brain, whereas others are direct; one speaks of the optic tract, rather than nerve, between the chiasma and the brain. Because of its position, the optic chiasma is damaged in tumors of the hypophysis.

ORGANIZER

Chemical substance produced by an embryonic zone which brings about the differentiation of the nervous system in its vicinity.

PAIN

Behavior or specific reactions in response to disagreeable or dangerous excitations or situations; the reactions of pain are an unconscious automatism depending on the hypothalamus; it is a secondary repercussion on the brain that produces the sensation of pain. One can make pain disappear by suppressing cerebral sensitivity. Excitation of the brain is painless.

PATHOLOGICAL

What is contrary to the normal – that is, to nature. The goal of biology is to distinguish the normal from the pathological; this is difficult because the two may have the same external manifestations. It is necessary to make an over-all judgment of functional value. From the cerebral point of view, there are two kinds of pathological conditions, one resulting from a cerebral disturbance and the other resulting from using a normal brain badly.

PATTERNS

(spatio-temporal or dynamic)
Physiological architectures or structurations fluctuating between excitations and inhibitions, associating or separating cerebral neurons in time and space, basis of sensations, bodily movements, thoughts, etc. Called *dynamic stereotypes* in Pavlovian terminology. Example: corporeal schema or image of self.
Synonym: *structurations.*

PAVLOVISM

Pavlovian neurophysiology: the importance of the nervous system in diseases, the role of conditioned reflexes and therefore of acquisitions that modify what is innate, the curative effect of sleep, painless childbirth, etc.

PERSONALIZATION

The totality of phenomena which, in terms of biological or embryological evolution or particularly in the physiology of the brain, make possible the appearance of reflective consciousness, control, and freedom.

POLARIZATION

Existence of an electric charge on the surface of a living cell, positive on the outside, owing to the existence of a difference of ionic concentration. Any excitation is a temporary depolarization. Inhibition is accompanied by superpolarization.

PONS (pons Varoli)

Part of the encephalon between the mesencephalon and the medulla oblongata, connected with the cerebellum by the middle cerebellar peduncles.

PRAXIA

Meaningful bodily movement. Ensemble of conditioned reflexes providing the co-ordination of the psychomotor neurons for the execution of a complex act that has been learned. Its disappearance is an apraxia. Kinds: motor aphasia or anarthria in the case of spoken language, agraphia in the case of writing.

PREFRONTAL REGION

This part of the brain, which is the most highly developed in man, is the brain of control, judgment, moral conscience. It is the supreme organ of personalization, connecting the affective part (rhinencephalon) and reason (noetic brain) to make a complete man, capable of heartfelt emotions and love. It is this region that is eliminated by a lobotomy.

PRIMATES
Zoological order of mammals including monkeys, apes, and man.

PSYCHIATRY
The medical specialty dealing with mental disturbances.

PSYCHISM
Designates the psychological activity as a whole, making it possible to avoid the metaphysical word soul or spirit. See also: *behavior*.

PSYCHOANALYSIS
Method of treating neuroses by exploring the unconscious by means of spontaneous awareness of repressed memories. Is based upon the work of Freud, who assigns too much importance to the genital aspect. Other schools: Adler, inferiority complex, role of the social; Jung, archetypes of the primitive psychism; etc.

PSYCHOSIS
Psychological disorder with serious disturbance of consciousness, synonymous with mental or psychiatric disease. As opposed to neurosis.

PSYCHOSOMATIC
This adjective designates the influence of what is mental on what is physical in the unity of the individual. It should be identified with *cerebrovisceral*.

PSYCHOSURGERY
Brain surgery intended to cure mental and temperamental disturbances. Typical example: lobotomy. As opposed to neurosurgery.

PSYCHOTHERAPY
Therapeutic treatment of psychic or psychosomatic disturbances by psychological approaches (dialogue, suggestion, confidence, etc.) – a humane way of restoring equilibrium to the brain. The active psychotherapies involving a stimulation of awareness may be contrasted to the passive psychotherapies of suggestion.

PULSATIONS (nervous)
Rhythmic succession of impulsions or waves of nervous impulses.

PYRAMIDAL NEURONS
Name given, because of the shape of the cell body, to the psychomotor neurons of the brain whose axon acts directly upon the peripheral motor neurons (pyramidal bundle). The name extrapyramidal is given to the other cerebral motor neurons and to those associated with them in the base of the brain (extrapyramidal tracts).

RADIOGRAPHY
X ray photography of internal organs.

REANIMATION
Transition from latent life (apparent death) to normal life. Is not at all a resurrection (miracle of a dead man's return to life).

REASON
Quality of human reflective consciousness making possible critical intellectual knowledge. Provided by the verbalized cerebral integration of the noetic brain.

RED NUCLEUS
Important nucleus of gray matter at the base of the mesencephalon under the aqueduct of Sylvius; center that regulates muscular tonus, connected with the spinal cord and subjected to the influence of the cerebellum. Its destruction causes decerebralized rigidity, contracture in the form of extension.

REFLEX
The basis of nervous functioning: reflex arc – nervous pathway including a sensory neuron, central neurons, and a motor neuron; reflex act – muscular or glandular response to a sensory excitation. The reflex act is a complex automatic process involving self-regulated medullary structurations.

REFLEXOTHERAPY
Therapy designed to treat centers

or organs by sensory excitation, the source of reflexes. Example: cupping glasses, synesthesia, acupuncture, nasal reflexotherapy. By extension: re-education of conditioned reflexes.

REFRACTORY PERIOD
Phase of unexcitability following the activity of a neuron or muscle; it limits the frequency of nervous pulsations.

RELATION (life of)
Behavior in the external environment, as opposed to "life of nutrition."

RELAXATION
Soothing therapy involving a slackening of muscular tonus. There exist several types. Includes a certain amount of psychotherapy.

REPRESSION
An impossibility of being aware of distressing memories, a source of psychosomatic disturbances; this psychoanalytical term is based on a cerebral inhibition.

RETICULAR FORMATION
Column of diffuse gray matter surrounding the anatomically denser nuclei, extending from the medulla to the thalamus and continuing in the diffuse thalamic system. It is a network of small, multifariously interconnected neurons, forming paths with numerous relays. Sensory impulses, coming from all parts, converge upon it, to play an activating role. Since the work of Magoun, it has been known to be the activating, regulating, and harmonizing system of all nervous functioning, working down toward the spinal cord and up toward the brain (center of wakefulness). Alongside the activating formation, there exists an inhibitive formation in the medulla. The reticular formation intervenes in the selective excitations and inhibitions of attention and conditioned reflexes. It is very sensitive to chemical influences.

RHEOBASIS
Minimum threshold of strength for a sufficiently long electric excitation.

RHINENCEPHALON
Means olfactory brain. It is the exclusively olfactory primitive brain of the lower vertebrates which has become, in man, the brain of instinct and affectivity. Is to be opposed to the neocortex. Very complex system including notably the limbic convolution encircling the center of the hemisphere on its inner surface. The olfactory zone is limited to the terminal point of the olfactory fibers coming from the olfactory bulb. The rhinencephalon acts through the hypothalamus.

SELF-REGULATION
Adaptation of functioning to needs, not by an external correction but by an internal automatism in which every effect exerts a retroactive influence upon its cause. Self-regulation is a characteristic held in common by modern machines, the adult as as well as the embryological organism, and the brain.

SENSATION
Elementary state of consciousness informing us of the stimulation of an organ of the senses; their co-ordination produces perception. Sensation is judged by behavior or, in man, by what he says about it. Sensation is the awareness of a cerebral pattern which is the reflection of sensorial excitation. The existence of a pattern of sensation therefore does not depend on awareness.

SENSORIAL MESSAGE
Since Adrian, it has been known that sensorial impressions are carried from the receptor organs to the brain in the form of successions of nervous impulsions whose frequency is proportionate to the intensity of excitation. The same is true of motor messages.

SEROTONINE
Substance involved in cerebral functioning and playing a role in

psychiatry. Is related to the chemical mediators.

SHOCK
In neurophysiology, violent and unbalancing disturbance of the regulatory centers of the base of the brain that are responsible for sympathetic and endocrinal equilibrium, muscular tonus, affectivity, and consciousness; leads therefore to psychic and psychosomatic disturbances. The shock can come from the outer environment, the inner environment, or the psychism; certain shocks are used in psychiatric therapy (electric shock).

SIGNALING (systems of)
In Pavlovian terminology, the term "first signaling system" is used to designate the conditioned reflexes of thought by images, the term "second signaling system" to designate those of language.

SLEEP
Physiological inhibition of the brain and the basal centers, in function protectively restful, suspending consciousness and volition and disturbing the psychism (dreams).

SOMATOPLASM
Neuronic cell body with the nucleus; it gives birth to the impulse.

SOMATOTOPY
Cerebral localizations; point-by-point representation of the cutaneous surface or muscles in the cerebral zones, the cortical retina, the cortical cochlea. The somatotopy of the neocortex forms a contrast to the diffuse arrangements of the primitive brain.

SOUL
Metaphysical word designating the spiritual part of man or, by extension, the psychism of animals. Is often interpreted as being synonymous with psychism; neurophysiology knows only the cerebral conditions of the soul. From the biological point of view, the soul is actually more than the psychism because it expresses the unity of the individual and his originality, present before the brain, from the egg stage on, and subsisting after the destruction of the brain. Materialists believe that the soul has no existence of its own and disappears at death, the disintegration of the individual; idealists give rational arguments for its separate reality and survival.

STATISTICS
Every biological value is a mean value based on large numbers, but one must take into account normal divergences (frequent and rare) and pathological deviations (abnormal).

STEREOTAXIS
Method of localizing in space, making it possible to locate a point inside the brain.

STRESS
Word used by Hans Selye. Nonspecific reaction of the organism to any external, internal, or psychic aggression or shock; it is a hypothalamic disequilibrium. Artificial hibernation prevents it. The organism becomes sick in order to defend its equilibrium (disease of adaptation syndrome).

STRUCTURATION
See: *patterns (spatio-temporal or dynamic).* Physiological and dynamic term, whereas *structure* is anatomical and static.

STUPEFACIENTS
Cerebral toxicants that reduce pain and cause hallucinations, a factor in toxicomania: morphine, cocaine, hashish, peyotl, etc.

SUBCONSCIOUS
That which is momentarily not present in consciousness.

SUBLIMATION
Camouflage of an unconscious complex, making possible an indirect awareness of it; process brought to light by psychoanalysis, it is a conditioned reflex. Sublimation is a false cure.

SUGGESTION
Behavior or thought caused by

the influence of someone else without one's being conscious of this influence. Is accompanied by hypnotic sleep in suggestion-prone subjects. Has a therapeutic efficacity (conditioned reflexes of language). One variety is self-suggestion, as opposed to reflective awareness.

SYMPATHETIC SYSTEM
Nervous system of the "life of nutrition," called vegetative or autonomic. Is made up of the orthosympathetic (the sympathetic system in the strict sense) and the parasympathetic.

SYNAPSE (or synapsis)
Point of contact (contiguity without continuity) between two neurons (fiber and soma, dendrites, etc.). Seat of the processes of nervous transmission with chemical mediation. This phenomenon takes a certain amount of time, called the synaptic delay. In a strict sense, the synapses are interneuronic. Included with them is the motor end-plate, the juncture between the motor nerve and the striped muscle.

TELENCEPHALON
Embryological term designating the cerebral hemispheres and the corpora striata as opposed to the diencephalon.

THALAMUS
Or optical layer. Central gray sensory nucleus belonging to the diencephalon, the relay point for all the sensorial tracts except olfaction; center of co-ordination of the cerebral cortex, regulatory center through the diffuse thalamic system extending the reticular formation.

THERMOREGULATION
Ensemble of mechanisms ensuring the maintenance in birds and mammals of a constant internal temperature (homothermy) by control of the production and loss of heat. Depends on a center which is located in the hypothalamus and which is paralyzed in artificial hibernation.

THOUGHT
From the neurophysiological point of view, thought is based upon the unrolling of neuronic patterns inside the cerebral cortex. There exist two kinds: thought by images, which is common to both animals and man, and verbalized thought, which is peculiar to man.

TOPECTOMY
See: *lobotomy*.

TOXICOMANIA
Poisoning by stupefacients, accompanied by getting used to them; involves a state of need and serious withdrawal disturbances.

TRANQUILIZERS
Soothing medicaments for anxiety and emotivity, less active than the neuroleptics. Synonym: *"happiness pills."*

TRANSCENDENT
Metaphysical term which indicates that a phenomenon is of a nature that belongs to a different order than its manifestations or conditions. Idealism professes the transcendence of the human soul. Is opposed to immanent, but transcendence can be accompanied by separation (command from the outside) or immanence (internal animating presence). Science observes emergences but cannot diagnose whether they are true cases of transcendence.

TREPANATION
Perforation of the skull for neurophysiological exploration or surgical operation.

TRUTH SERUM
See: *narcoanalysis*.

UNCONSCIOUS
That which eludes consciousness, such as the area of visceral sensitivities and acts, elementary cerebral mechanisms, repressed memories and thoughts (Freud). By extension, that which eludes it momentarily (subconscious), what one is inattentive to or what is habitual.

VITAMINS
Chemical molecules that, in small quantities, are indispensable to life. The organism must find them in its alimentation. They contribute to the synthesis of diastases. Lack or excess of vitamins may lead to disturbances, particularly of a nervous or psychic nature.

WALLERIAN DEGENERATION
Named after A. Waller, who discovered it. Disappearance of the axon and myelin in the part of a sectioned fiber that has been separated from the cell body; in nerves, the fiber is subsequently regenerated and once more fills the sheaths. Makes it possible to locate the cell body.

WAVES OF THE ELECTROENCEPHALOGRAM
Types of periodic electric activity in the brain, of varying amplitude and frequency. The alpha waves are the waves of sensorial and intellectual repose, waves of preponderantly occipital synchronization; the beta waves are less ample and more frequent, and have a parietofrontal maximum; the delta waves are the slow waves of sleep and cerebral suffering; the theta waves, which are somewhat more rapid, are connected with emotivity and anger.

WHITE MATTER
As opposed to gray matter. Part of the nerve centers that contains only myelinized nerve fibers grouped in bundles and ensuring conduction.

WILL (or volition)
Domination of cerebral transmission of impulses (motoricity) by consciousness for execution or control.

WOLF-CHILDREN
Children reared by wolves and dehumanized (India). They run about on all fours and howl. It is only with difficulty that they can be re-educated to speak a language.

YOGA
Hindu technique of psychophysical control, having as its goal mental control.

Selected Bibliography

Adrian, E. D.: *The Physical Background of Perception*. New York, Oxford University Press, 1947.

Ashby, W. R.: *Design for a Brain*. London, Chapman and Hall, 1952.

Bailey, Percival, and Gerhardt von Bonin: *The Isocortex of Man*. Urbana, University of Illinois Press, 1951.

Bonin, Gerhardt von: *Essay on the Cerebral Cortex*. Springfield (Ill.), Charles C. Thomas, 1950.

Brazier, M. A. B.: *The Electrical Activity of the Nervous System*. London, Pitman, 1951.

Fulton, John F.: *Functional Localization in the Frontal Lobes and Cerebellum*. New York, Oxford University Press, 1949.

———: *Physiology of the Nervous System*. New York, Oxford University Press, 1943 (second edition).

Gesell, Arnold Lucius: *Infant Development; The Embryology of Early Human Behavior*. New York, Harper, 1952.

Gibbs, F. A. and E. L.: *Atlas of Electroencephalography*. Cambridge (Mass.), Addison-Wesley, 1950.

Hill, J. D. N., and G. Parr (*ed.*): *Electroencephalography*. London, Macdonald, 1950.

Hubbard, R. L.: *Dianetics, the Modern Science of Mental Health*. New York, Hermitage Press, 1951.

Huxley, Julian Sorell: *Evolution in Action*. New York, Harper, 1953.

Jeffress, Lloyd A. (*ed.*): *Cerebral Mechanisms in Behavior*. New York, Wiley, 1951.

Laslett, Peter (*ed.*): *The Physical Basis of Mind*. Oxford, Basil Blackwell, 1950.

Olmsted, J. M. D.: *Claude Bernard, Physiologist*. London, Cassell, 1939.

Penfield, W., and T. Rasmussen: *The Cerebral Cortex of Man*. New York, Macmillan, 1950.

Pfeiffer, John: *The Human Brain*. New York, Harper, 1955.

Piéron, Henri: *The Sensations; Their Functions, Processes and Mechanisms*. Translated by M. H. Pirenne and B. C. Abott. New Haven, Yale University Press, 1952.

Prenant, Marcel: *Biology and Marxism*. Translated by C. Desmond Greaves. New York, International Publishers, 1938.

Ranson, Stephen W.: *The Anatomy of the Nervous System*. Philadelphia, W. B. Saunders, 1954.

Richter, D. (*ed.*): *Perspectives in Neuropsychiatry*. London, H. K. Lewis, 1950.

Rostand, Jean: *Can Man Be Modified?* Translated by Jonathan Griffin. New York, Basic Books, 1959.

Teilhard de Chardin, Pierre: *The Phenomenon of Man*. Translated by Bernard Wall. New York, Harper, 1959.

Walter, W. Grey: *The Living Brain*. New York, Norton, 1953.

Wiener, Norbert: *Cybernetics*. New York, Wiley, 1948.

———: *The Human Use of Human Beings*. Boston, Houghton Mifflin, 1950.

Acknowledgments

Illustrations are from the following sources: B.N. (Éd. du Seuil): pp. 3, 4, 8a, 10b, 11a, 12a, 14, 92; Archives Dr. Chauchard (Éd. du Seuil): pp. 8b, 10b, 17, 18, 19a and b, 21, 22, 26, 34, 36, 40, 43, 48, 49, 51, 53, 54a and b, 55b, 57, 66, 67, 68, 74b, 77, 83, 88, 97, 134; Regards: p. 159; Atlas Photo: pp. 141, 146; U.S.I.S.: pp. 27, 30, 143, 157, 170; Keystone: p. 155; René Bouillot (C.S.F.): p. 28; Science et Vie: pp. 74a, 78; Rapho: pp. 75, 132, 147; Doisneau-Rapho: p. 150; Éd. du Seuil (diagrams): pp. 9, 12b, 16, 20, 23, 24, 32, 37, 47, 55a, 63, 69, 71, 72, 85, 86, 90, 96, 104, 105, 106, 108, 109, 113; Fritz Kahn: inside back cover, 123, 127; Roger Roche (Éd. du Seuil): inside front cover.

The author and editor wish to thank Editions Hachette who authorized permission to reproduce the illustrations 11a and 119, taken from *L'Intelligence des animaux* by Marcel Sire.

The translator wishes to thank Dr. Karl H. Niebyl for his assistance in checking the translation.